DYLAN THOMAS

Selected Writings

Edited by

J. P. HARRIES

HEINEMANN EDUCATIONAL BOOKS

LONDON

Heinemann Educational Books Ltd
22 Bedford Square, London WC1B 3HH
LONDON EDINBURGH MELBOURNE AUCKLAND
HONG KONG SINGAPORE KUALA LUMPUR NEW DELHI
IBADAN NAIROBI JOHANNESBURG
EXETER (NH) KINGSTON PORT OF SPAIN

ISBN 0 435 13890 1

First published 1970
Reprinted 1977, 1980

Reminiscences of Childhood (second version), *Memories of Christmas*, *A Visit to Grandpa's*, *A Story*, *Patricia, Edith and Arnold*, *Extraordinary Little Cough*, *The Followers*, *After the Fair*, *The Visitor*, *The International Eisteddfod* here reprinted by arrangement with J. M. Dent & Sons Ltd and the Trustees for the Copyrights of the late Dylan Thomas

Adventures in the Skin Trade first published by Putnam & Co. 1955, here reprinted slightly abridged by arrangement with the Trustees for the Copyrights of the late Dylan Thomas

Published by Heinemann Educational Books Ltd
Set, printed and bound in Great Britain by
Fakenham Press Limited, Fakenham, Norfolk

CONTENTS

INTRODUCTION

WHEN he visited New York in 1950, Dylan Thomas proclaimed his individuality by declaring, 'First I am a Welshman.' This is not the way we are accustomed to think of him; we think of him first as a poet and the author of *Under Milk Wood*, and only secondly as a Welshman. Thomas, whose lifelong theme as a writer was himself, knew the order of priorities. He knew what he owed as a writer to his background, which was more than is often the case, and rightly placed it first.

Dylan Marlais Thomas was born on 27 October 1914, at No. 5 Cwmdonkin Drive, which is in that part of Swansea called the Uplands. In view of the pattern of Dylan Thomas's life it is well to consider his family background. His father was a teacher of English at Swansea Grammar School. He had wanted to be a poet, but perhaps because he had been unable to communicate through his poetry he became a heavy drinker. By some enormous effort of will he had cured himself. It seems that his son inherited this tendency (did he similarly despair of reaching others with his best work?) for in the last years of his life Dylan Thomas was very nearly an alcoholic.

As a child Thomas was sickly. He suffered from severe lung haemorrhages, but had grown out of this by the time he went to Swansea Grammar School at the age of ten. However, he was left with scarred lungs and a tendency to bronchitis. From the age of fifteen, when he started chain-smoking, he developed asthma. When he was eighteen a doctor told him that unless he drank less and smoked less he would be dead in four years.

In view of his delicate health it was inevitable that his mother should spoil him. In his early years he could go to school only when he was well enough, and his parents chose to send him to a private school. His academic career at Swansea Grammar School was not particularly distinguished except for his contributions to the school magazine. Before he left at the age of eighteen he was already working for the then *South Wales Daily Post*, but his firm intention was to earn his living as a poet. He left the staff of the paper after two years but continued to contribute to its columns as a freelance. He had left school in July 1931, and his first visit to London was in November 1934. Those three intervening years were perhaps the most important in his life; they cover the creative period for the bulk of his poetry, and most of the prose pieces in this volume.

He began to gain a reputation as a poet, but lived a wild and impulsive life, often in conditions of extreme poverty. But in 1937 two events occurred that were to shape the rest of his life. On 4 April of that year he made his first broadcast and on 11 July he married Caitlin Macnamara. In broadcasting he found an ideal medium for his speaking voice and for his rich personality. And, of course, broadcasting paid in a way that poetry did not. Now that he was married the need to earn became acute, so the coincidence of his being launched into broadcasting and into marriage at one and the same time seemed providential. However, it marked the beginning of a process whereby Thomas the poet became supplanted by Dylan the Entertainer. Thomas was to describe himself as 'good old three-adjectives-a-penny belly-churning Thomas, the Rimbaud of Cwmdonkin Drive'. Rimbaud completed his poetry before the age of twenty – never writing another line until his death.

Because of the state of his lungs he did not serve in the war, and it was during this period that he began to write film scripts. After the war he became more famous as a broadcaster. He made his first visit to America in February 1950, as a lecturer, and made his fourth and last in October 1953. By this time he was drinking heavily and his health was failing. He collapsed in New York in the November 1953 and died of pneumonia on the 9th. He was brought back to Wales and his body is buried in Laugharne. He was forty years old.

The two most important places in Thomas's life were Cwmdonkin Park and Fern Hill. The one was opposite his house; the other was near Llangain, where he went to spend his holidays in the remote countryside with his Aunt Ann. The house where he stayed has a grisly history; it was once the property of a public hangman who committed suicide by hanging himself in one of the rooms. While staying at that house Dylan had the pleasure of terrifying himself and it gave him a chance to experiment with the macabre. These two places, together with the Gower peninsula, are important to us because, with the exception of *Adventures in the Skin Trade*, they provide the background for the stories in this book.

It was from these two sources, himself and his experiences, and his Welsh background, that Dylan Thomas created his prose works and poems. He inherited the power and passion of his countrymen. His father was a sceptic, but his grandfather was a preacher. The chapel and its imagery, the great books and poems it has made its own, *The Pilgrim's Progress* and the Bible, the hymns and great prayers, all left their mark on his imagination and their stamp on his vocabulary. He attended chapel as a boy and revolted against it, but by then the language and feeling had gripped him, and he remained, like D. H. Lawrence, a non-Christian protestant.

He came from a community in which conversation and story-telling is a natural activity and is almost an art form in its own right. It would be natural for him to select his material and order it in the most telling way. But he was not concerned with telling a story – that is, he was not concerned with a plot of cause and effect. His theme is people, either himself or others around him, and provided the personality is rich enough, the eccentricity sufficiently engaging, then that will suffice, even if what he relates is not, in formal terms, a story at

all. 'A Story' exemplifies this. There is a loose narrative thread
– the chronology of a day out – but what we are chiefly inter-
ested in is the characters on the trip. The conversation near the
end, about who played rugby for Aberavon in 1898, shows, in
encapsulated form, Thomas's method and purpose. In 'A Visit
to Grandpa's' we are left with Grandpa standing on the
bridge. There is no further development of the story. To
Thomas there is no need; the re-creation of Grandpa, his
presentation as a complete character, is both the purpose and
justification for writing the piece.

Thomas's poetry was very carefully worked. When he was
writing verse he would begin each line on a fresh piece of
paper, which would give him plenty of room for alteration and
emendation. His prose writing was no less meticulously worked
but the method was different. He liked to see the completed piece as a whole, like a poem. Sometimes he would take a
cardboard box and open it out, for in this way he got a sufficiently large area to work on, and write the whole piece on it in
tiny writing. If he was using ordinary notepaper he would put
the succeeding pieces on the wall so that he could see the total
effect. This unusual, no doubt unique method of composition
shows that these prose pieces are not casually thrown off, the
by-products of a mind relaxing from more serious poetic work,
but are as carefully considered as anything else he wrote.

His gift seems to be lyrical, in that he wishes to capture the
mood where several personalities are in harmony or agree-
ment, or are faced with a situation which they grasp together.
It is the moment he is concerned with, and the feelings of
individuals at that moment. We have the end of 'A Story'
where the men gambol in the moonlight. At the end of 'The
Followers' comes the awful moment for the watchers when
Katinka asks, 'Why are those two boys looking in at the
window?' There is the scene in 'After the Fair' when the men
from the caravans find the Fat Man and the girl in black with a
baby in her arms, racing round and round on the mechanical
horses. It is characteristic that the moment has been prepared

for, and has the power to give the story the quality of an experience felt and seen by the reader. The underlying movement of ideas in these pieces is poetic, for their logic is not founded in the world of cause and effect and time.

Thomas was present at the Surrealist Exhibition in 1936. There is no doubt that he did not take the movement seriously. He went along to join in the fun. He boiled some string which he passed round in cups, asking politely, 'Weak or strong?' His association with this movement has led to the opinion that Thomas was a surrealist – that is, a writer who abandons the control of the conscious part of his mind, letting images spill from the unconscious mind on to the page without rational regulation. In fact, Thomas was always a deliberate craftsman, but he used the imagery of the unconscious mind in his own way. There is, of course, a bizarre element in his work, which is found especially in *Adventures in the Skin Trade* and 'The Visitors'.

It is *Adventures in the Skin Trade* which may be considered the most surrealist of his work. The theme of the novel, which was never finished, is an account of a man who peels off layer after layer of what lies without (his 'skins') until at last only the naked man is left; the truth is established. Samuel Bennet, the hero, makes a journey to London as a raw provincial, much as Dylan Thomas had done himself, and the author intended him to meet fantastic adventures, not because he sought them, but because they came to meet him. Each adventure was to remove another skin until at length Samuel was to find himself back at Paddington Station, naked. There were to be seven skins or layers in all. Thomas wrote only three chapters, but it is easy to see what he had in mind even from the slightly abridged version printed here. In a way, the book is a pilgrimage to self-knowledge for Samuel Bennet, and there is no doubt that Thomas drew heavily on his own experiences as a provincial in London when he was writing it. It is significant that he began it in 1936, when the surrealist influence was at its greatest.

The eleven pieces in this anthology have been arranged in an autobiographical order, not in order of composition. They progress from childhood to manhood. From the earliest, 'Reminiscences of Childhood', to *Adventures in the Skin Trade* they show the development of Thomas's mind, the growth of awareness of the world around him. [The only exception to this is 'International Eisteddfod', which has been included as an example of Thomas's journalistic style.]

J. P. HARRIES

PART ONE

Autobiographical Stories

REMINISCENCES OF CHILDHOOD
(Second Version)

I LIKE very much people telling me about their childhood, but they'll have to be quick or else I'll be telling them about mine.

I was born in a large Welsh town at the beginning of the Great War – an ugly, lovely town, or so it was and is to me; crawling, sprawling by a long and splendid curving shore where truant boys and Sandfield boys and old men from nowhere, beachcombed, idled, and paddled, watched the dock-bound ships or the ships steaming away into wonder and India, magic and China, countries bright with oranges and loud with lions, threw stones into the sea for the barking outcast dogs; made castles and forts and harbours and race tracks in the sand; and on Saturday summer afternoons listened to the brass band, watched the Punch and Judy, or hung about on the fringes of the crowd to hear the fierce religious speakers who shouted at the sea, as though it were wicked and wrong to roll in and out like that, white-horsed and full of fishes.

One man, I remember, used to take off his hat and set fire to his hair every now and then, but I do not remember what it proved, if it proved anything at all, except that he was a very interesting man.

This sea-town was my world; outside a strange Wales, coal-pitted, mountained, river-run, full so far as I knew, of choirs and football teams and sheep and story-book tall black hats and red flannel petticoats, moved about its business which was none of mine.

Beyond that unknown Wales with its wild names like peals of bells in the darkness, and its mountain men clothed in the skins

of animals perhaps and always singing, lay England which was
London and the country called the Front, from which many of
our neighbours never came back. It was a country to which
only young men travelled.

At the beginning the only front I knew was the little lobby
before our front door. I could not understand how so many
people never returned from there, but later I grew to know
more, though still without understanding, and carried a wooden
rifle in the park and shot down the invisible unknown enemy
like a flock of wild birds. And the park itself was a world within
the world of the sea-town. Quite near where I lived, so near
that on summer evenings I could listen in my bed to the voices
of older children playing ball on the sloping paper-littered
bank, the park was full of terrors and treasures. Though it was
only a little park, it held within its borders of old tall trees,
notched with our names and shabby from our climbing, as
many secret places, caverns and forests, prairies and deserts, as
a country somewhere at the end of the sea.

And though we would explore it one day, armed and des-
perate, from end to end, from the robbers' den to the pirates'
cabin, the highwayman's inn to the cattle ranch, or the hidden
room in the undergrowth, where we held beetle races, and lit
the wood fires and roasted potatoes and talked about Africa
and the makes of motor-cars, yet still the next day it remained
as unexplored as the Poles – a country just born and always
changing.

There were many secret societies but you could belong only
to one, and in blood or red ink, and a rusty pocket-knife, with,
of course, an instrument to remove stones from horses' feet,
you signed your name at the foot of a terrible document, swore
death to all the other societies, crossed your heart that you
would divulge no secret and that if you did, you would consent
to torture by slow fire, and undertook to carry out by yourself a
feat of either daring or endurance. You could take your choice:
would you climb to the top of the tallest and most dangerous
tree, and from there hurl stones and insults at grown-up passers-

by, especially postmen, or any other men in uniform? Or would you ring every doorbell in the terrace, not forgetting the doorbell of the man with the red face who kept dogs and ran fast? Or would you swim in the reservoir, which was forbidden and had angry swans, or would you eat a whole old jam-jar full of mud?

There were many more alternatives. I chose one of endurance and for half an hour, it may have been longer or shorter, held up off the ground a very heavy broken pram we had found in a bush. I thought my back would break and the half-hour felt like a day, but I preferred it to braving the red face and the dogs, or to swallowing tadpoles.

We knew every inhabitant of the park; every regular visitor; every nursemaid; every gardener; every old man. We knew the hour when the alarming retired policeman came in to look at the dahlias and the hour when the old lady arrived in the bath-chair with six pekinese, and a pale girl to read aloud to her. I think she read the newspaper, but we always said she read the *Wizard*. The face of the old man who sat summer and winter on the bench looking over the reservoir I can see clearly now, and I wrote a poem long long after I'd left the park and the seatown called: 'The Hunchback in the Park'.

> The Hunchback in the Park
> A solitary mister
> Propped between trees and water
> From the opening of the garden lock
> That lets the trees and water enter
> Until the Sunday sombre bell at dark.
>
> Eating bread from a newspaper
> Drinking water from the chained cup
> That the children filled with gravel
> In the fountain basin where I sailed my ship
> Slept at night in a dog kennel
> But nobody chained him up.

Like the park birds he came early
Like the water he sat down
And Mister they called Hey mister
The truant boys from the town
Running when he had heard them clearly
On out of sound

Past lake and rockery
Laughing when he shook his paper
Through the loud zoo of the willow groves
Hunchbacked in mockery
Dodging the park keeper
With his stick that picked up leaves.

And the old dog sleeper
Alone between nurses and swans
While the boys among willows
Made the tigers jump out of their eyes
To roar on the rockery stones
And the groves were blue with sailors.

Made all day until bell time
A woman's figure without fault
Straight as a young elm
Straight and tall from his crooked bones
That she might stand in the night
After the locks and the chains

All night in the unmade park
After the railings and shrubberies
The birds the grass the trees and the lake
And the wild boys innocent as strawberries
Had followed the hunchback
To his kennel in the dark.

And that park grew up with me; that small world widened
as I learned its secrets and boundaries, as I discovered new

refuges and ambushes in its woods and jungles; hidden homes and lairs for the multitudes of imagination, for cowboys and Indians, and the tall terrible half-people who rode on night-mares through my bedroom. But it was not the only world – that world of rockery, gravel path, playbank, bowling-green, bandstands, reservoir, dahlia garden, where an ancient keeper, known as Smoky, was the whiskered snake in the grass one must keep off. There was another world where with my friends I used to dawdle on half holidays along the bent and Devon-facing seashore, hoping for gold watches or the skull of a sheep or a message in a bottle to be washed up with the tide; and another where we used to wander whistling through the packed streets, stale as station sandwiches, round the impressive gas-works and the slaughter-house, past by the blackened monu-ments and the museum that should have been in a museum. Or we scratched at a kind of cricket on the bald and cindery surface of the recreation ground, or we took a tram that shook like an iron jelly down to the gaunt pier, there to clamber under the pier, hanging perilously on to its skeleton legs or to run along to the end where patient men with the seaward eyes of the dockside unemployed capped and mufflered, dangling from their mouths pipes that had long gone out, angled over the edge for unpleasant-tasting fish.

Never was there such a town as ours, I thought, as we fought on the sand-hills with rough boys or dared each other to climb up the scaffolding of half-built houses soon to be called Labur-num or The Beeches. Never was there such a town, I thought, for the smell of fish and chips on Saturday evenings; for the Saturday afternoon cinema matinées where we shouted and hissed our threepences away; for the crowds in the streets with leeks in their hats on international nights; for the park, the inexhaustible and mysterious, bushy Red-Indian hiding park where the hunchback sat alone and the groves were blue with sailors. The memories of childhood have no order, and so I remember that never was there such a dame school as ours, so firm and kind and smelling of galoshes, with the sweet and

fumbled music of the piano lessons drifting down from upstairs to the lonely schoolroom, where only the sometimes tear-
ful wicked sat over undone sums, or to repent a little crime –
the pulling of a girl's hair during geography, the sly shin-kick
under the table during English literature. Behind the school was
a narrow lane where only the oldest and boldest threw pebbles
at windows, scuffled and boasted, fibbed about their relations:

'My father's got a chauffeur.'

'What's he want a chauffeur for, he hasn't got a car.'

'My father's the richest man in the town.'

'My father's the richest man in Wales.'

'My father owns the world.'

And swopped gob-stoppers for slings, old knives for mar-
bles, kite-string for foreign stamps.

The lane was always the place to tell your secrets; if you
did not have any you invented them: occasionally now I dream
that I am turning out of school into the lane of confidences
when I say to the boys of my class, 'At last, I have a real secret.'

'What is it? What is it?'

'I can fly.'

And when they do not believe me, I flap my arms and slowly
leave the ground, only a few inches at first, then gaining air
until I fly waving my cap level with the upper windows of the
school, peering in until the mistress at the piano screams and
the metronome falls to the ground and stops, and there is no
more time.

And I fly over the trees and chimneys of my town, over the
dockyards skimming the masts and funnels, over Inkerman
Street, Sebastopol Street, and the street where all the women
wear men's caps, over the trees of the everlasting park, where a
brass band shakes the leaves and sends them showering down
on to the nurses and the children, the cripples and the idlers,
and the gardeners, and the shouting boys: over the yellow seashore, and the stone-chasing dogs, and the old men, and the
singing sea.

The memories of childhood have no order, and no end.

MEMORIES OF CHRISTMAS

ONE CHRISTMAS was so much like another, in those years,
around the sea-town corner now, and out of all sound except
the distant speaking of the voices I sometimes hear a moment
before sleep, that I can never remember whether it snowed for
six days and six nights when I was twelve or whether it snowed
for twelve days and twelve nights when I was six; or whether
the ice broke and the skating grocer vanished like a snowman
through a white trap-door on that same Christmas Day that
the mince-pies finished Uncle Arnold and we tobogganed
down the seaward hill, all the afternoon, on the best tea-tray,
and Mrs Griffiths complained, and we threw a snowball at her
niece, and my hands burned so, with the heat and the cold,
when I held them in front of the fire, that I cried for twenty
minutes and then had some jelly.

All the Christmases roll down the hill towards the Welsh-
speaking sea, like a snowball growing whiter and bigger and
rounder, like a cold and headlong moon bundling down the
sky that was our street; and they stop at the rim of the ice-
edged, fish-freezing waves, and I plunge my hands in the
snow and bring out whatever I can find; holly or robins or
pudding, squabbles and carols and oranges and tin whistles,
and the fire in the front room, and bang go the crackers, and
holy, holy, holy, ring the bells, and the glass bells shaking on
the tree, and Mother Goose, and Struwelpeter – oh! the baby-
burning flames and the clacking scissorman! – Billy Bunter and
Black Beauty, Little Women and boys who have three helpings,
Alice and Mrs Potter's badgers, penknives, tedddy-bears –
named after a Mr Theodore Bear, their inventor, or father, who

died recently in the United States – mouth-organs, tin-soldiers, and blancmange, and Auntie Bessie playing 'Pop Goes the Weasel' and 'Nuts in May' and 'Oranges and Lemons' on the untuned piano in the parlour all through the thimble-hiding musical-chairing blind-man's-buffing party at the end of the never-to-be-forgotten day at the end of the unremembered year.

In goes my hand into that wool-white bell-tongued ball of holidays resting at the margin of the carol-singing sea, and out come Mrs Prothero and the firemen.

It was on the afternoon of the day of Christmas Eve, and I was in Mrs Prothero's garden, waiting for cats, with her son Jim. It was snowing. It was always snowing at Christmas; December, in my memory, is white as Lapland, though there were no reindeers. But there were cats. Patient, cold, and callous, our hands wrapped in socks, we waited to snowball the cats. Sleek and long as jaguars and terrible-whiskered, spitting and snarling they would slink and sidle over the white back-garden walls, and the lynx-eyed hunters, Jim and I, fur-capped and moccasined trappers from Hudson's Bay off Eversley Road, would hurl our deadly snowballs at the green of their eyes. The wise cats never appeared. We were so still, Eskimo-footed arctic marksmen in the muffling silence of the eternal snows – eternal, ever since Wednesday – that we never heard Mrs Prothero's first cry from her igloo at the bottom of the garden. Or, if we heard it at all, it was, to us, like the far-off challenge of our enemy and prey, the neighbour's Polar Cat. But soon the voice grew louder. 'Fire!' cried Mrs Prothero, and she beat the dinner-gong. And we ran down the garden, with the snowballs in our arms, towards the house, and smoke, indeed, was pouring out of the dining-room, and the gong was bombilating, and Mrs Prothero was announcing ruin like a town-crier in Pompeii. This was better than all the cats in Wales standing on the wall in a row. We bounded into the house, laden with snowballs, and stopped at the open door of the smoke-filled room. Something was burning all right; perhaps it was Mr Prothero, who always slept there after midday dinner with a newspaper over his face; but he was standing in the middle of the room, saying 'A fine Christmas!' and smacking at the smoke with a slipper.

'Call the fire-brigade,' cried Mrs Prothero as she beat the gong.

'They won't be there,' said Mr Prothero, 'it's Christmas.'

There was no fire to be seen, only clouds of smoke and Mr Prothero standing in the middle of them, waving his slipper as though he were conducting.

'Do something,' he said.

And we threw all our snowballs into the smoke – I think we missed Mr Prothero – and ran out of the house to the telephone-box.

'Let's call the police as well,' Jim said.

'And the ambulance.'

'And Ernie Jenkins, he likes fires.'

But we only called the fire-brigade, and soon the fire-engine came and three tall men in helmets brought a hose into the house and Mr Prothero got out just in time before they turned it on. Nobody could have had a noisier Christmas Eve. And when the firemen turned off the hose and were standing in the wet and smoky room, Jim's aunt, Miss Prothero, came downstairs and peered in at them. Jim and I waited, very quietly, to hear what she would say to them. She said the right thing, always. She looked at the three tall firemen in their shining helmets, standing among the smoke and cinders and dissolving snowballs, and she said: 'Would you like something to read?'

Now out of that bright white snowball of Christmas gone comes the stocking, the stocking of stockings, that hung at the foot of the bed with the arm of a golliwog dangling over the top and small bells ringing in the toes. There was a company, gallant and scarlet but never nice to taste though I always tried when very young, of belted and busbied and musketed lead soldiers so soon to lose their heads and legs in the wars on the kitchen table after the tea-things, the mince-pies, and the cakes that I helped to make by stoning the raisins and eating them, had been cleared away; and a bag of moist and many-coloured jelly-babies and a folded flag and a false nose and a tram-conductor's cap and a machine that punched tickets and rang a bell; never a catapult; once, by a mistake that no one could explain, a little hatchet; and a rubber buffalo, or it may have been a horse, with a yellow head and haphazard legs; and a celluloid duck that made, when you pressed it, a most un-ducklike noise, a mewing moo that an ambitious cat might make who wishes to be a cow; and a painting-book in which I could make the grass, the trees, the sea, and the animals any colour I pleased: and still the dazzling sky-blue sheep are grazing in the red field under a flight of rainbow-beaked and pea-green birds.

Christmas morning was always over before you could say Jack Frost. And look! suddenly the pudding was burning! Bang the gong and call the fire-brigade and the book-loving firemen! Someone found the silver threepenny-bit with a currant on it; and the someone was always Uncle Arnold. The motto in my cracker read:

> Let's all have fun this Christmas Day,
> Let's play and sing and shout hooray!

and the grown-ups turned their eyes towards the ceiling, and Auntie Bessie, who had already been frightened, twice, by a clockwork mouse, whimpered at the sideboard and had some elderberry wine. And someone put a glass bowl full of nuts on the littered table, and my uncle said, as he said once every year: 'I've got a shoe-nut here. Fetch me a shoe-horn to open it, boy.'

And dinner was ended.

And I remember that on the afternoon of Christmas Day, when the others sat around the fire and told each other that this was nothing, no, nothing, to the great snowbound and turkey-proud yule-log-crackling holly-berry-bedizened and kissing-under-the-mistletoe Christmas when *they* were children, I would go out, schoolcapped and gloved and mufflered, with my bright new boots squeaking, into the white world on to the seaward hill, to call on Jim and Dan and Jack and to walk with them through the silent snowscape of our town.

We went padding through the streets, leaving huge deep foot prints in the snow, on the hidden pavements.

'I bet people'll think there's been hippoes.'

'What would you do if you saw a hippo coming down Terrace Road?'

'I'd go like this, bang! I'd throw him over the railings and roll him down the hill and then I'd tickle him under the ear and he'd wag his tail . . .'

'What would you do if you saw *two* hippoes . . .?'

Iron-flanked and bellowing he-hippoes clanked and blundered and battered through the scudding snow towards us as we passed by Mr Daniel's house.

'Let's post Mr Daniel a snowball through his letter-box.'

'Let's write things in the snow.'

'Let's write "Mr Daniel looks like a spaniel" all over his lawn.'

'Look,' Jack said, 'I'm eating snow-pie.'

'What's it taste like?'

'Like snow-pie,' Jack said.

Or we walked on the white shore.

'Can the fishes see it's snowing?'

'They think it's the sky falling down.'

The silent one-clouded heavens drifted on to the sea.

'All the old dogs have gone.'

Dogs of a hundred mingled makes yapped in the summer at the sea-rim and yelped at the trespassing mountains of the waves.

'I bet St Bernards would like it now.'

And we were snowblind travellers lost on the north hills, and the great dewlapped dogs, with brandy-flasks round their necks, ambled and shambled up to us, baying 'Excelsior'.

We returned home through the desolate poor sea-facing

streets where only a few children fumbled with bare red fingers in the thick wheel-rutted snow and catcalled after us, their voices fading away, as we trudged uphill, into the cries of the dock-birds and the hooters of ships out in the white and whirling bay.

Bring out the tall tales now that we told by the fire as we roasted chestnuts and the gaslight bubbled low. Ghosts with their heads under their arms trailed their chains and said 'whooo' like owls in the long nights when I dared not look over my shoulder; wild beasts lurked in the cubby-hole under the stairs where the gas-meter ticked. 'Once upon a time,' Jim said, 'there were three boys, just like us, who got lost in the dark in the snow, near Bethesda Chapel, and this is what happened to them. . . .' It was the most dreadful happening I had ever heard.

And I remember that we went singing carols once, a night or two before Christmas Eve, when there wasn't the shaving of a moon to light the secret, white-flying streets. At the end of a long road was a drive that led to a large house, and we stumbled up the darkness of the drive that night, each one of us afraid, each one holding a stone in his hand in case, and all of us too brave to say a word. The wind made through the drive-trees noises as of old and unpleasant and maybe web-footed men wheezing in caves. We reached the black bulk of the house.

'What shall we give them?' Dan whispered.

'"Hark the Herald"? "Christmas comes but Once a Year"?'

'No,' Jack said: 'We'll sing "Good King Wenceslas." 'I'll count three.'

One, two, three, and we began to sing, our voices high and seemingly distant in the snow-felted darkness round the house that was occupied by nobody we knew. We stood close together, near the dark door.

> Good King Wenceslas looked out
> On the Feast of Stephen.

And then a small, dry voice, like the voice of someone who has not spoken for a long time, suddenly joined our singing: a small, dry voice from the other side of the door: a small, dry voice through the keyhole. And when we stopped running we were outside *our* house; the front room was lovely and bright; the gramophone was playing; we saw the red and white balloons hanging from the gas-bracket; uncles and aunts sat by the fire; I thought I smelt our supper being fried in the kitchen. Everything was good again, and Christmas shone through all the familiar town.

'Perhaps it was a ghost,' Jim said.

'Perhaps it was trolls,' Dan said, who was always reading.

'Let's go in and see if there's any jelly left,' Jack said. And we did that.

A VISIT TO GRANDPA'S

IN THE middle of the night I woke from a dream full of whips and lariats as long as serpents, and runaway coaches on mountain passes, and wide, windy gallops over cactus fields, and I heard the man in the next room crying, 'Gee-up!' and 'Whoa!' and trotting his tongue on the roof of his mouth.

It was the first time I had stayed in grandpa's house. The floor-boards had squeaked like mice as I climbed into bed, and the mice between the walls had creaked like wood as though another visitor was walking on them. It was a mild summer night, but curtains had flapped and branches beaten against the window. I had pulled the sheets over my head, and soon was roaring and riding in a book.

'Whoa there, my beauties!' cried grandpa. His voice sounded very young and loud, and his tongue had powerful hooves, and he made his bedroom into a great meadow. I thought I would see if he was ill, or had set his bedclothes on fire, for my mother had said that he lit his pipe under the blankets, and had warned me to run to his help if I smelt smoke in the night. I went on tiptoe through the darkness to his bedroom door, brushing against the furniture and upsetting a candlestick with a thump. When I saw there was a light in the room I felt frightened, and as I opened the door I heard grandpa shout, 'Gee-up!' as loudly as a bull with a megaphone.

He was sitting straight up in bed and rocking from side to side as though the bed were on a rough road; the knotted edges of the counterpane were his reins; his invisible horse stood in a shadow beyond the bedside candle. Over a white flannel nightshirt he was wearing a red waistcoat with walnut-sized brass buttons. The over-filled bowl of his pipe smouldered among his whiskers like a little, burning hayrick on a stick. At the sight of me, his hands dropped from the reins and lay blue and quiet, the bed stopped still on a level road, he muffled his tongue into silence, and the horses drew softly up.

'Is there anything the matter, grandpa?' I asked, though the clothes were not on fire. His face in the candlelight looked like a ragged quilt pinned upright on the black air and patched all over with goat-beards.

He stared at me mildly. Then he blew down his pipe, scattering the sparks and making a high, wet dog-whistle of the stem, and shouted: 'Ask no questions.'

After a pause, he said slyly: 'Do you ever have nightmares, boy?'

I said: 'No.'

'Oh, yes, you do,' he said.

I said I was woken by a voice that was shouting to horses.

'What did I tell you?' he said. 'You eat too much. Who ever heard of horses in a bedroom?'

He fumbled under his pillow, brought out a small tinkling bag, and carefully untied its strings. He put a sovereign in my hand, and said: 'Buy a cake.' I thanked him and wished him good night.

As I closed my bedroom door, I heard his voice crying loudly gaily, 'Gee-up! gee-up!' and the rocking of the travelling bed.

In the morning I woke from a dream of fiery horses on a plain that was littered with furniture, and of large, cloudy men who rode six horses at a time and whipped them with burning bed-clothes. Grandpa was at breakfast, dressed in deep black. After breakfast he said, 'There was a terrible loud wind last night,' and sat in his arm-chair by the hearth to make clay balls for the fire. Later in the morning he took me for a walk, through Johnstown village and into the fields on the Llanstephan road.

A man with a whippet said, 'There's a nice morning, Mr Thomas,' and when he had gone, leanly as his dog, into the short-treed green wood he should not have entered because of the notices, grandpa said: 'There, do you hear what he called you? Mister!'

We passed by small cottages, and all the men who leant on the gates congratulated grandpa on the fine morning. We passed through the wood full of pigeons, and their wings broke the branches as they rushed to the tops of the trees. Among the soft, contented voices and the loud, timid flying, grandpa said, like a man calling across a field: 'If you heard those old birds in the night, you'd wake me up and say there were horses in the trees.'

We walked back slowly, for he was tired, and the lean man stalked out of the forbidden wood with a rabbit held as gently over his arm as a girl's arm in a warm sleeve.

On the last day but one of my visit I was taken to Llanstephan in a governess cart pulled by a short, weak pony. Grandpa might have been driving a bison, so tightly he held the reins, so ferociously cracked the long whip, so blasphemously shouted warning to boys who played in the road, so stoutly stood with his gaitered legs apart and cursed the demon strength and wilfulness of his tottering pony.

'Look out, boy!' he cried when we came to each corner, and pulled and tugged and jerked and sweated and waved his whip like a rubber sword. And when the pony had crept miserably round each corner, grandpa turned to me with a sighing smile: 'We weathered that one, boy.'

When we came to Llanstephan village at the top of the hill, he left the cart by the Edwinsford Arms and patted the pony's muzzle and gave it sugar, saying: 'You're a weak little pony, Jim, to pull big men like us.'

He had strong beer and I had lemonade, and he paid Mrs Edwinsford with a sovereign out of the tinkling bag; she inquired after his health, and he said that Llangadock was better for the tubes. We went to look at the churchyard and the sea, and sat in the wood called the Sticks, and stood on the concert platform in the middle of the wood where visitors sang on midsummer nights and, year by year, the innocent of the village was elected mayor. Grandpa paused at the churchyard and pointed over the iron gate at the angelic headstones and the poor wooden crosses. 'There's no sense in lying there,' he said.

We journeyed back furiously: Jim was a bison again.

I woke late on my last morning, out of dreams where the Llanstephan sea carried bright sailing-boats as long as liners; and heavenly choirs in the Sticks, dressed in bards' robes and brass-buttoned waistcoats, sang in a strange Welsh to the departing sailors. Grandpa was not at breakfast; he rose early. I walked in the fields with a new sling, and shot at the Towy gulls and the rooks in the parsonage trees. A warm wind blew from the summer points of the weather; a morning mist climbed from the ground and floated among the trees and hid the noisy birds; in the mist and the wind my pebbles flew lightly up like hailstones in a world on its head. The morning passed without a bird falling.

I broke my sling and returned for the midday meal through the parson's orchard. Once, grandpa told me, the parson had bought three ducks at Carmarthen Fair and made a pond for them in the centre of the garden, but they waddled to the gutter under the crumbling doorsteps of the house, and swam and quacked there. When I reached the end of the orchard path, I looked through a hole in the hedge and saw that the parson had made a tunnel through the rockery that was between the gutter and the pond and had set up a notice in plain writing: 'This way to the pond.'

The ducks were still swimming under the steps.

Grandpa was not in the cottage. I went into the garden, but grandpa was not staring at the fruit-trees. I called across to a man who leant on a spade in the field beyond the garden hedge: 'Have you seen my grandpa this morning?'

He did not stop digging, and answered over his shoulder: 'I seen him in his fancy waistcoat.'

Griff, the barber, lived in the next cottage. I called to him through the open door: 'Mr Griff, have you seen my grand-pa?'

The barber came out in his shirt sleeves.

I said: 'He's wearing his best waistcoat.' I did not know if it was important, but grandpa wore his waistcoat only in the night.

'Has grandpa been to Llanstephan?' asked Mr Griff anxiously.

'He went there yesterday in a little trap,' I said.

He hurried indoors and I heard him talking in Welsh, and he came out again with his white coat on, and he carried a striped and coloured walking-stick. He strode down the village street and I ran by his side.

When we stopped at the tailor's shop, he cried out, 'Dan!' and Dan Tailor stepped from his window where he sat like an Indian priest but wearing a derby hat. 'Dai Thomas has got his waistcoat on,' said Mr Griff, 'and he's been to Llanstephan.'

As Dan Tailor searched for his overcoat, Mr Griff was striding on. 'Will Evans,' he called outside the carpenter's shop, 'Dai Thomas has been to Llanstephan, and he's got his waistcoat on.'

'I'll tell Morgan now,' said the carpenter's wife out of the hammering, sawing darkness of the shop.

We called at the butcher's shop and Mr Price's house, and Mr Griff repeated his message like a town-crier.

We gathered together in Johnstown square. Dan Tailor had his bicycle, Mr Price his pony trap. Mr Griff, the butcher, Morgan carpenter, and I climbed into the shaking trap, and we trotted off towards Carmarthen town. The tailor led the way, ringing his bell as though there were a fire or a robbery, and an old woman by the gate of a cottage at the end of the street ran inside like a pelted hen. Another woman waved a bright handkerchief.

'Where are we going?' I asked.

Grandpa's neighbours were as solemn as old men with black hats and jackets on the outskirts of a fair. Mr Griff shook his head and mourned: 'I didn't expect this again from Dai Thomas.'

'Not after last time,' said Mr Price sadly.

We trotted on, we crept up Constitution Hill, we rattled down into Lammas Street, and the tailor still rang his bell and a dog ran, squealing, in front of his wheels. As we clip-clopped over the cobbles that led down to the Towy bridge, I remembered grandpa's nightly noisy journeys that rocked the bed and shook the walls, and I saw his gay waistcoat in a vision and his patchwork head tufted and smiling in the candlelight. The tailor before us turned round on his saddle, his bicycle wobbled and skidded. 'I see Dai Thomas!' he cried.

The trap rattled on to the bridge, and I saw grandpa there: the buttons of his waistcoat shone in the sun, he wore his tight black Sunday trousers and a tall, dusty hat I had seen in a cupboard in the attic, and he carried an ancient bag. He bowed to us. 'Good morning, Mr Price,' he said, 'and Mr Griff and Mr Morgan and Mr Evans.' To me he said: 'Good morning, boy.'

Mr Griff pointed his coloured stick at him.

'And what do you think you are doing on Carmarthen bridge in the middle of the afternoon,' he said sternly, 'with your best waistcoat and your old hat?'

Grandpa did not answer, but inclined his face to the river wind, so that his beard was set dancing and wagging as though he talked, and watched the coracle men move, like turtles, on the shore.

Mr Griff raised his stunted barber's pole. 'And where do you think you are going,' he said, 'with your old black bag?'

Grandpa said: 'I am going to Llangadock to be buried.' And he watched the coracle shells slip into the water lightly, and the gulls complain over the fish-filled water as bitterly as Mr Price complained:

'But you aren't dead yet, Dai Thomas.'

For a moment grandpa reflected, then: 'There's no sense in lying dead in Llanstephan,' he said. 'The ground is comfy in

Llangadock; you can twitch your legs without putting them in the sea.'

His neighbours moved close to him. They said: 'You aren't dead, Mr Thomas.'

'How can you be buried, then?'

'Nobody's going to bury you in Llanstephan.'

'Come on home, Mr Thomas.'

'There's strong beer for tea.'

'And cake.'

But grandpa stood firmly on the bridge, and clutched his bag to his side, and stared at the flowing river and the sky, like a prophet who has no doubt.

A STORY

IF YOU can call it a story. There's no real beginning or end and there's very little in the middle. It is all about a day's outing, by charabanc, to Porthcawl, which, of course, the charabanc never reached, and it happened when I was so high and much nicer.

I was staying at the time with my uncle and his wife. Although she was my aunt, I never thought of her as anything but the wife of my uncle, partly because he was so big and trumpeting and red-hairy and used to fill every inch of the hot little house like an old buffalo squeezed into an airing cupboard, and partly because she was so small and silk and quick and made no noise at all as she whisked about on padded paws, dusting the china dogs, feeding the buffalo, setting the mouse-traps that never caught her; and once she sleaked out of the room, to squeak in a nook or nibble in the hayloft, you forgot she had never been there.

But there he was, always, a steaming hulk of an uncle, his braces straining like hawsers, crammed behind the counter of the tiny shop at the front of the house, and breathing like a brass band; or guzzling and blustery in the kitchen over his gutsy supper, too big for everything except the great black boats of his boots. As he ate, the house grew smaller; he billowed out over the furniture, the loud check meadow of his waistcoat littered, as though after a picnic, with cigarette-ends, peelings, cabbage stalks, birds' bones, gravy; and the forest fire of his hair crackled among the hooked hams from the ceiling. She was so small she could hit him only if she stood on a chair, and every Saturday night at half past ten he would lift her up, under his arm, on to a chair in the kitchen so that she could hit him on the head with whatever was handy, which was always a china dog. On Sundays, and when pickled, he sang high tenor, and had won many cups.

The first I heard of the annual outing was when I was sitting one evening on a bag of rice behind the counter, under one of my uncle's stomachs, reading an advertisement for sheep-dip, which was all there was to read. The shop was full of my uncle, and when Mr Benjamin Franklyn, Mr Weazley, Noah Bowen, and Will Sentry came in, I thought it would burst. It was like all being together in a drawer that smelt of cheese and turps, and twist tobacco and sweet biscuits and snuff and waistcoat. Mr Benjamin Franklyn said that he had collected enough money for the charabanc and twenty cases of pale ale and a pound apiece over that he would distribute among the members of the outing when they first stopped for refreshment, and he was about sick and tired, he said, of being followed by Will Sentry.

'All day long, wherever I go,' he said, 'he's after me like a collie with one eye. I got a shadow of my own *and* a dog. I don't need no Tom, Dick, or Harry pursuing me with his dirty muffler on.'

Will Sentry blushed, and said: 'It's only oily. I got a bicycle.'

'A man has no privacy at all,' Mr Franklyn went on. 'I tell you he sticks so close I'm afraid to go out the back in case I sit in his lap. It's a wonder to me,' he said, 'he don't follow me into bed at night.'

'Wife won't let,' Will Sentry said.

And that started Mr Franklyn off again, and they tried to soothe him down by saying: 'Don't you mind Will Sentry' . . . 'No harm in old Will' . . . 'He's only keeping an eye on the money, Benjie.'

'Aren't I honest?' asked Mr Franklyn in surprise. There was no answer for some time, then Noah Bowen said: 'You know what the committee is. Ever since Bob the Fiddle they don't feel safe with a new treasurer.'

'Do you think *I*'m going to drink the outing funds, like Bob the Fiddle did?' said Mr Franklyn.

'You *might*,' said my uncle slowly.

'I resign,' said Mr Franklyn.

'Not with our money you won't,' Will Sentry said.

'Who put dynamite in the salmon pool?' said Mr Weazley, but nobody took any notice of him. And, after a time, they all began to play cards in the thickening dusk of the hot, cheesy shop, and my uncle blew and bugled whenever he won, and Mr Weazley grumbled like a dredger, and I fell to sleep on the gravy-scented mountain meadow of uncle's waistcoat.

On Sunday evening, after Bethesda, Mr Franklyn walked into the kitchen where my uncle and I were eating sardines witH spoons from the tin because it was Sunday and his wife would not let us play draughts. She was somewhere in the kitchen, too. Perhaps she was inside the grandmother clock, hanging from the weights and breathing. Then, a second later, the door opened again and Will Sentry edged into the room, twiddling his hard, round hat. He and Mr Franklyn sat down on the settee, stiff and moth-balled and black in their chapel and funeral suits.

'I brought the list,' said Mr Franklyn. 'Every member fully paid. You ask Will Sentry.'

My uncle put on his spectacles, wiped his whiskery mouth with a handkerchief big as a Union Jack, laid down his spoon of sardines, took Mr Franklyn's list of names, removed the spectacles so that he could read, and then ticked the names off one by one.

'Enoch Davies. Aye. He's good with his fists. You never know. Little Gerwain. Very melodious bass. Mr Cadwalladwr. That's right. He can tell opening time better than my watch. Mr Weazley. Of course. He's been to Paris. Pity he suffers so much in the charabanc. Stopped us nine times last year between the Beehive and the Red Dragon. Noah Bowen, ah, very peaceable. He's got a tongue like a turtle-dove. Never a argument with Noah Bowen. Jenkins Loughor. Keep him off economics. It cost a plate-glass window. And ten pints for the Sergeant. Mr Jervis. Very tidy.'

'He tried to put a pig in the charra,' Will Sentry said.

'Live and let live,' said my uncle.

Will Sentry blushed.

'Sinbad the Sailor's Arms. Got to keep in with him. Old O. Jones.'

'Why old O. Jones?' said Will Sentry.

'Old O. Jones always goes,' said my uncle.

I looked down at the kitchen table. The tin of sardines was gone. By Gee, I said to myself, Uncle's wife is quick as a flash.

'Cuthbert Johnny Fortnight. Now there's a card,' said my uncle.

'He whistles after women,' Will Sentry said.

'So do you,' said Mr Benjamin Franklyn, 'in your mind.'

My uncle at last approved the whole list, pausing only to say, when he came across one name: 'If we weren't a Christian community, we'd chuck that Bob the Fiddle in the sea.'

'We can do that in Porthcawl,' said Mr Franklyn, and soon after that he went, Will Sentry no more than an inch behind him, their Sunday-bright boots squeaking on the kitchen cobbles.

And then, suddenly, there was my uncle's wife standing in front of the dresser, with a china dog in one hand. By Gee, I said to myself again, did you ever see such a woman, if that's what she is. The lamps were not lit yet in the kitchen and she stood in a wood of shadows, with the plates on the dresser behind her shining – like pink-and-white eyes.

'If you go on that outing on Saturday, Mr Thomas,' she said to my uncle in her small, silk voice, 'I'm going home to my mother's.'

Holy Mo, I thought, she's got a mother. Now that's one old bald mouse of a hundred and five I won't be wanting to meet in a dark lane.

'It's me or the outing, Mr Thomas.'

I would have made my choice at once, but it was almost

half a minute before my uncle said: 'Well, then, Sarah, it's the outing, my love.' He lifted her up, under his arm, on to a chair in the kitchen, and she hit him on the head with the china dog. Then he lifted her down again, and then I said good night.

For the rest of the week my uncle's wife whisked quiet and quick round the house with her darting duster, my uncle blew and bugled and swole, and I kept myself busy all the time being up to no good. And then at breakfast time on Saturday morning, the morning of the outing, I found a note on the kitchen table. It said: 'There's some eggs in the pantry. Take your boots off before you go to bed.' My uncle's wife had gone, as quick as a flash.

When my uncle saw the note, he tugged out the flag of his handkerchief and blew such a hubbub of trumpets that the plates on the dresser shook. 'It's the same every year,' he said. And then he looked at me. 'But this year it's different. *You*'ll have to come on the outing, too, and what the members will say I dare not think.'

The charabanc drew up outside, and when the members of the outing saw my uncle and me squeeze out of the shop together, both of us cat-licked and brushed in our Sunday best, they snarled like a zoo.

'Are you bringing a *boy*?' asked Mr Benjamin Franklyn as we climbed into the charabanc. He looked at me with horror.

'Boys is nasty,' said Mr Weazley.

'He hasn't paid his contributions,' Will Sentry said.

'No room for boys. Boys get sick in charabancs.'

'So do you, Enoch Davies,' said my uncle.

'Might as well bring *women*.'

The way they said it, women were worse than boys.

'Better than bringing grandfathers.'

'Grandfathers is nasty too,' said Mr Weazley.

'What can we do with him when we stop for refreshments?'

'I'm a grandfather,' said Mr Weazley.

'Twenty-six minutes to opening time,' shouted an old man

in a panama hat, not looking at a watch. They forgot me at once.

'Good old Mr Cadwalladwr,' they cried, and the charabanc started off down the village street.

A few cold women stood at their doorways, grimly watching us go. A very small boy waved good-bye, and his mother boxed his ears. It was a beautiful August morning.

We were out of the village, and over the bridge, and up the hill towards Steeplehat Wood when Mr Franklyn, with his list of names in his hand, called out loud: 'Where's old O. Jones?'

'Where's old O?'

'We've left old O behind.'

'Can't go without old O.'

And though Mr Weazley hissed all the way, we turned and drove back to the village, where, outside the Prince of Wales, old O. Jones was waiting patiently and alone with a canvas bag.

'I didn't want to come at all,' old O. Jones said as they hoisted him into the charabanc and clapped him on the back and pushed him on a seat and stuck a bottle in his hand, 'but I always go.' And over the bridge and up the hill and under the deep green wood and along the dusty road we wove, slow cows and ducks flying by, until 'Stop the bus!' Mr Weazley cried. 'I left my teeth on the mantelpiece.'

'Never you mind,' they said, 'you're not going to bite nobody,' and they gave him a bottle with a straw.

'I might want to smile,' he said.

'Not you,' they said.

'What's the time, Mr Cadwalladwr?'

'Twelve minutes to go,' shouted back the old man in the panama, and they all began to curse him.

The charabanc pulled up outside the Mountain Sheep, a small, unhappy public-house with a thatched roof like a wig with ringworm. From a flagpole by the Gents fluttered the flag of Siam. I knew it was the flag of Siam because of cigarette cards. The landlord stood at the door to welcome us, simpering like a wolf. He was a long, lean, black-fanged man with a greased love-curl and pouncing eyes. 'What a beautiful August day!' he said, and touched his love-curl with a claw. That was the way he must have welcomed the Mountain Sheep before he ate it, I said to myself. The members rushed out, bleating, and into the bar.

'You keep an eye on the charra,' my uncle said: 'see nobody steals it now.'

'There's nobody to steal it,' I said, 'except some cows,' but my uncle was gustily blowing his bugle in the bar. I looked at the cows opposite, and they looked at me. There was nothing else for us to do. Forty-five minutes passed, like a very slow cloud. The sun shone down on the lonely road, the lost, un-wanted boy, and the lake-eyed cows. In the dark bar they were so happy they were breaking glasses. A Shoni-Onion Breton man, with a beret and a necklace of onions, bicycled down the road and stopped at the door.

'Quelle un grand matin, monsieur,' I said.

'There's French, boy bach!' he said.

I followed him down the passage, and peered into the bar. I could hardly recognize the members of the outing. They had all changed colour. Beetroot, rhubarb, and puce, they hollered and rollicked in that dark, damp hole like enormous ancient bad boys, and my uncle surged in the middle, all red whiskers and bellies. On the floor was broken glass and Mr Weazley.

'Drinks all round,' cried Bob the Fiddle, a small, absconding man with bright blue eyes and a plump smile.

'Who's been robbing the orphans?'

'Who sold his little babby to the gyppoes?'

'Trust old Bob, he'll let you down.'

'You will have your little joke,' said Bob the Fiddle, smiling like a razor, 'but I forgive you, boys.'

Out of the fug and babel I heard: 'Come out and fight.'

'No, not now, later.'

'No, now when I'm in a temper.'

'Look at Will Sentry, he's proper snobbled.'

'Look at his wilful feet.'

'Look at Mr Weazley lording it on the floor.'

Mr Weazley got up, hissing like a gander. 'That boy pushed me down deliberate,' he said, pointing to me at the door, and I slunk away down the passage and out to the mild, good cows. Time clouded over, the cows wondered, I threw a stone at them and they wandered, wondering, away. Then out blew my uncle, ballooning, and one by one the members lumbered after him in a grizzle. They had drunk the Mountain Sheep dry. Mr Weazley had won a string of onions that the Shoni-Onion man raffled in the bar. 'What's the good of onions if you left your teeth on the mantelpiece?' he said. And when I looked through the back window of the thundering charabanc, I saw the pub grow smaller in the distance. And the flag of Siam, from the flagpole by the Gents, fluttered now at half mast.

The Blue Bull, the Dragon, the Star of Wales, the Twll in the Wall, the Sour Grapes, the Shepherd's Arms, the Bells of Aberdovey: I had nothing to do in the whole, wild August world but remember the names where the outing stopped and keep an eye on the charabanc. And whenever it passed a public-house, Mr Weazley would cough like a billygoat and cry: 'Stop the bus, I'm dying of breath!' And back we would all have to go.

Closing time meant nothing to the members of that outing. Behind locked doors, they hymned and rumpused all the beautiful afternoon. And, when a policeman entered the Druid's Tap by the back door, and found them all choral with beer, 'Sssh!' said Noah Bowen, 'the pub is shut.'

'Where do you come from?' he said in his buttoned, blue voice.

They told him.

'I got a auntie there,' the policeman said. And very soon he was singing 'Asleep in the Deep.'

Off we drove again at last, the charabanc bouncing with tenors and flagons, and came to a river that rushed along among willows.

'Water!' they shouted.

'Porthcawl!' sang my uncle.

'Where's the donkeys?' said Mr Weazley.

And out they lurched, to paddle and whoop in the cool, white, winding water. Mr Franklyn, trying to polka on the slippery stones, fell in twice. 'Nothing is simple,' he said with dignity as he oozed up the bank.

'It's cold!' they cried.

'It's lovely!'

'It's smooth as a moth's nose!'

'It's *better* than Porthcawl!'

And dusk came down warm and gentle on thirty wild, wet, pickled, splashing men without a care in the world at the end of the world in the west of Wales. And, 'Who goes there?' called Will Sentry to a wild duck flying.

They stopped at the Hermit's Nest for a rum to keep out the cold. 'I played for Aberavon in 1898,' said a stranger to Enoch Davies.

'Liar,' said Enoch Davies.

'I can show you photos,' said the stranger.

'Forged,' said Enoch Davies.

'And I'll show you my cap at home.'

'Stolen.'

'I got friends to prove it,' the stranger said in a fury.

'Bribed,' said Enoch Davies.

On the way home, through the simmering moon-splashed dark, old O. Jones began to cook his supper on a primus stove in the middle of the charabanc. Mr Weazley coughed himself blue in the smoke. 'Stop the bus,' he cried, 'I'm dying of breath!' We all climbed down into the moonlight. There was not a public-house in sight. So they carried out the remaining cases, and the primus stove, and old O. Jones himself, and took them into a field, and sat down in a circle in the field and drank and sang while old O. Jones cooked sausage and mash and the moon flew above us. And there I drifted to sleep against my uncle's mountainous waistcoat, and, as I slept, 'Who goes there?' called out Will Sentry to the flying moon.

PATRICIA, EDITH, AND ARNOLD

THE SMALL boy in his invisible engine, the Cwmdonkin Special, its wheels, polished to dazzle, crunching on the small back garden scattered with breadcrumbs for the birds and white with yesterday's snow, its smoke rising thin and pale as breath in the cold afternoon, hooted under the wash-line, kicked the dog's plate at the washhouse stop, and puffed and pistoned slower and slower while the servant girl lowered the pole, unpegged the swinging vests, showed the brown stains under her arms, and called over the wall: 'Edith, Edith, come here, I want you.'

Edith climbed on two tubs on the other side of the wall and called back: 'I'm here, Patricia.' Her head bobbed up above the broken glass.

He backed the Flying Welshman from the washhouse to the open door of the coal-hole and pulled hard on the brake that was a hammer in his pocket: assistants in uniform ran out with fuel; he spoke to a saluting fireman, and the engine shuffled off, round the barbed walls of China that kept the cats away, by the frozen rivers in the sink, in and out of the coal-hole tunnel. But he was listening carefully all the time, through the squeals and whistles, to Patricia and the next-door servant, who belonged to Mrs Lewis, talking when they should have been working, calling his mother Mrs T., being rude about Mrs L.

He heard Patricia say: 'Mrs T won't be back till six.'

And Edith next door replied: 'Old Mrs L. has gone to Neath to look for Mr Robert.'

'He's on the randy again,' Patricia whispered.

'Randy, sandy, bandy!' cried the boy out of the coal-hole.

'You get your face dirty, I'll kill you,' Patricia said absent-mindedly.

She did not try to stop him when he climbed up the coal-heap. He stood quietly on the top, King of the Coal Castle, his head touching the roof, and listened to the worried voices of the girls. Patricia was almost in tears, Edith was sobbing and rocking on the unsteady tubs. 'I'm standing on top of the coal,' he said, and waited for Patricia's anger.

She said: 'I don't want to see him, you go alone.'

'We must, we must go together,' said Edith. 'I've got to know.'

'I don't want to know.'

'I can't stand it, Patricia, you must go with me.'

'You go alone, he's waiting for you.'

'Please, Patricia!'

'I'm lying on my face in the coal,' said the boy.

'No, it's your day with him. I don't want to know. I just want to think he loves me.'

'Oh, talk sense, Patricia, please! Will you come or no? I've got to hear what he says.'

'All right then, in half an hour. I'll shout over the wall.'

'You'd better come soon,' the boy said, 'I'm dirty as Christ knows what.'

Patricia ran to the coal-hole. 'The language! Come out of there at once!' she said.

The tubs began to slide and Edith vanished.

'Don't you dare use language like that again. Oh! your suit!' Patricia took him indoors.

She made him change his suit in front of her. 'Otherwise there's no telling.' He took off his trousers and danced around her, crying: 'Look at me, Patricia!'

'You be decent,' she said, 'or I won't take you to the park.'

'Am I going to the park, then?'

'Yes, we're all going to the park; you and me and Edith next door.'

He dressed himself neatly, not to annoy her, and spat on his hands before parting his hair. She appeared not to notice his silence and neatness. Her large hands were clasped together; she stared down at the white brooch on her chest. She was a tall, thick girl with awkward hands, her fingers were like toes, her shoulders were wide as a man's.

'Am I satisfactory?' he asked.

'There's a long word,' she said, and looked at him lovingly. She lifted him up and seated him on the top of the chest of drawers. 'Now you're as tall as I am.'

'But I'm not so old,' he said.

He knew that this was an afternoon on which anything might happen; it might snow enough for sliding on a tray; uncles from America, where he had no uncles, might arrive with revolvers and St Bernards; Ferguson's shop might catch on fire and all the piece-packets fall on the pavements; and he was not surprised when she put her black, straight-haired heavy head on his shoulder and whispered into his collar: 'Arnold, Arnold Matthews.'

'There, there,' he said, and rubbed her parting with his finger and winked at himself in the mirror behind her and looked down her dress at the back.

'Are you crying?'

'No.'

'Yes you are, I can feel the wet.'

She dried her eyes on her sleeve. 'Don't you let on that I was crying.'

'I'll tell everybody, I'll tell Mrs T. and Mrs L., I'll tell the policeman and Edith and my dad and Mr Chapman, Patricia was crying on my shoulder like a nanny goat, she cried for two hours, she cried enough to fill a kettle. I won't really,' he said.

As soon as he and Patricia and Edith set off for the park, it began to snow. Big flakes unexpectedly fell on the rocky hill, and the sky grew dark as dusk though it was only three in the afternoon. Another boy, somewhere in the allotments behind the houses, shouted as the first flakes fell. Mrs Ocky Evans opened the top bay-windows of Springmead and thrust her head and hands out, as though to catch the snow. He waited, without revolt, for Patricia to say, 'Quick! hurry back, it's snowing!' and to pack him in out of the day before his feet were wet. Patricia can't have seen the snow, he thought at the top of the hill, though it was falling heavily, sweeping against her face, covering her black hat. He dared not speak for fear of waking her, as they turned the corner into the road that led down to the park. He lagged behind to take his cap off and catch the snow in his mouth.

'Put on your cap,' said Patricia, turning, 'Do you want to catch your death of cold?'

She tucked his muffler inside his coat, and said to Edith: 'Will he be there in the snow, do you think? He's bound to be there, isn't he? He was always there on my Wednesdays, wet or fine.' The tip of her nose was red, her cheeks glowed like coals, she looked handsomer in the snow than in the summer, when her hair would lie limp on her wet forehead and a warm patch spread on her back.

'He'll be there,' Edith said. 'One Friday it was pelting down and he was there. He hasn't got anywhere else to go, he's always there. Poor Arnold!' She looked white and tidy in a coat with a fur piece, and twice as small as Patricia; she stepped through the thick snow as though she were going shopping.

'Wonders will never cease,' he said aloud to himself. This was Patricia letting him walk in the snow, this was striding along in a storm with two big girls. He sat down in the road. 'I'm on a sledge,' he said, 'pull me, Patricia, pull me like an Eskimo.'

'Up you get, you moochin, or I'll take you home.'

He saw that she did not mean it. 'Lovely Patricia, beautiful Patricia,' he said, 'pull me along on my bottom.'

'Any more dirty words, and you know who I'll tell.'

'Arnold Matthews,' he said.

Patricia and Edith drew closer together.

'He notices everything,' Patricia whispered.

Edith said: 'I'm glad I haven't got your job.'

'Oh,' said Patricia, catching him by the hand and pressing it on her arm, 'I wouldn't change him for the world!'

He ran down the gravel path on to the upper walk of the park. 'I'm spoilt!' he shouted, 'I'm spoilt! Patricia spoils me!'

Soon the park would be white all over; already the trees were blurred round the reservoir and fountain, and the training college on the gorse hill was hidden in a cloud. Patricia and Edith took the steep path down to the shelter. Following on the forbidden grass, he slid past them straight into a bare bush, but the bump and the pricks left him shouting and unhurt. The girls gossiped sadly now. They shook their coats in the deserted shelter, scattering snow on the seats, and sat down, close together still, outside the bowling-club window.

'We're only just on time,' said Edith. 'It's hard to be punctual in the snow.'

'Can I play by here?'

Patricia nodded. 'Play quietly then; don't be rough with the snow.'

'Snow! snow! snow!' he said, and scooped it out of the gutter and made a small ball.

'Perhaps he's found a job,' Patricia said.

'Not Arnold.'

'What if he doesn't come at all?'

'He's bound to come, Patricia; don't say things like that.'

'Have you brought your letters?'

'They're in my bag. How many have you got?'

'No, how many have you got, Edith?'

'I haven't counted.'

'Show me one of yours,' Patricia said.

He was used to their talk by this time; they were old and cuckoo, sitting in the empty shelter sobbing over nothing. Patricia was reading a letter and moving her lips.

'He told me that, too,' she said, 'that I was his star.'

'Did he begin: "Dear Heart?"'

'Always: "Dear Heart."'

Edith broke into real loud tears. With a snowball in his hand, he watched her sway on the seat and hide her face in Patricia's snowy coat.

Patricia said, patting and calming Edith, rocking her head: 'I'll give him a piece of my mind when he comes!'

When who comes? He threw the snowball high into the silently driving fall. Edith's crying in the deadened park was clear and thin as a whistle, and, disowning the soft girls and standing away from them in case a stranger passed, a man with boots to his thighs, or a sneering, bigger boy from the Uplands, he piled the snow against the wire of the tennis court and thrust his hands into the snow like a baker making bread. As he delved and moulded the snow into loaves, saying under his breath, 'This is the way it is done, ladies and gentlemen,' Edith raised her head and said: 'Patricia, promise me, don't be cross with him. Let's all be quiet and friendly.'

'Writing, "Dear Heart" to us both,' said Patricia angrily. 'Did he ever take off your shoes and pull your toes and —'

'No, no, you mustn't, don't go on, you mustn't speak like that!' Edith put her fingers to her cheeks. 'Yes, he did,' she said.

'Somebody has been pulling Edith's toes,' he said to himself, and ran round the other side of the shelter, chuckling. 'Edith went to market,' he laughed aloud, and stopped at the sight of a young man without an overcoat sitting in the corner seat and cupping his hand and blowing into them. The young man wore a white muffler and a check cap. When he saw the boy, he pulled his cap down over his eyes. His hands were pale blue and the ends of his finger yellow.

The boy ran back to 'Patricia, there's a man!' he cried.

'Where's a man?'

'On the other side of the shelter; he hasn't got an overcoat and he's blowing in his hands like this.'

Edith jumped up. 'It's Arnold!'

'Arnold Matthews, Arnold Matthews, we know you're there!' Patricia called round the shelter, and, after a long minute, the young man, raising his cap and smiling, appeared at the corner and leant against a wooden pillar.

The trousers of his sleek blue suit were wide at the bottoms; the shoulders were high and hard, and sharp at the ends; his pointed patent shoes were shining; a red handkerchief stuck from his breast pocket; he had not been out in the snow.

'Fancy you two knowing each other,' he said loudly, facing the red-eyed girls and the motionless, open-mouthed boy who stood at Patricia's side with his pockets full of snow-balls.

Patricia tossed her head and her hat fell over one eye. As she straightened her hat, 'You come and sit down here, Arnold Matthews, you've got some questions to answer!' she said in her washing-day voice.

Edith clutched at her arm: 'Oh! Patricia you promised.' She picked at the edge of her handkerchief. A tear rolled down her cheek.

Arnold said softly then: 'Tell the little boy to run away and play.'

The boy ran round the shelter once and returned to hear Edith saying: 'There's a hole in your elbow, Arnold,' and to see the young man kicking the snow at his feet and staring at the names and hearts cut on the wall behind the girls' heads.

'Who did you walk out with on Wednesdays?' Patricia asked. Her clumsy hands held Edith's letter close to the sprinkled folds of her chest.

'You, Patricia.'

'Who did you walk out with on Fridays?'

'With Edith, Patricia.'

He said to the boy: 'Here, son, can you roll a snowball as big as a football?'

'Yes, as big as two footballs.'

Arnold turned back to Edith, and said: 'How did you come to know Patricia Davies? You work in Brynmill.'

'I just started work in Cwmdonkin,' she said. 'I haven't seen you since, to tell you. I was going to tell you today, but I found out. How could you, Arnold? Me on my afternoon off, and Patricia on Wednesdays.'

The snowball had turned into a short snowman with a lopsided, dirty head and a face full of twigs, wearing a boy's cap and smoking a pencil.

'I didn't mean any harm,' said Arnold. 'I love you both.'

Edith screamed. The boy jumped forward and the snowman with a broken back collapsed.

'Don't tell your lies, how can you love two of us?' Edith cried, shaking her handbag at Arnold. The bag snapped open, and a bundle of letters fell on the snow.

'Don't you dare pick up those letters,' Patricia said.

Arnold had not moved. The boy was searching for his pencil in the snowman's ruins.

'You make your choice, Arnold Matthews, here and now.'

'Her or me,' said Edith.

Patricia turned her back to him. Edith, with her bag in her hand hanging open, stood still. The sweeping snow turned up the top page of a letter.

'You two,' he said, 'you go off the handle. Sit down and talk. Don't cry like that, Edith. Hundreds of men love more than one woman, you're always reading about it. Give us a chance, Edith, there's a girl.'

Patricia looked at the hearts and arrows and old names. Edith saw the letters curl.

'It's you, Patricia,' said Arnold.

Still Patricia stood turned away from him. Edith opened her mouth to cry, and he put a finger to his lips. He made the shape of a whisper, too soft for Patricia to hear. The boy watched him soothing and promising Edith, but she screamed again and ran out of the shelter and down the path, her handbag beating against her side.

'Patricia,' he said, 'turn round to me. I had to say it. It's you, Patricia.'

The boy bent down over the snowman and found his pencil

driven through its head. When he stood up he saw Patricia and Arnold arm in arm.

Snow dripped through his pockets, snow melted in his shoes, snow trickled down his collar into his vest. 'Look at you now,' said Patricia, rushing to him and holding him by the hands, 'you're wringing wet.'

'Only a bit of snow,' said Arnold, suddenly alone in the shelter.

'A bit of snow indeed, he's as cold as ice and his feet are like sponges. Come on home at once!'

The three of them climbed the path to the upper walk, and Patricia's footprints were large as a horse's in the thickening snow.

'Look, you can see our house, it's got a white roof!'

'We'll be there, ducky, soon.'

'I'd rather stay out and make a snowman like Arnold Matthews.'

'Hush! hush! your mother'll be waiting. You must come home.'

'No she won't. She gone on a randy with Mr Robert. Randy, sandy, bandy!'

'You know very well she's shopping with Mrs Partridge, you mustn't tell wicked lies.'

'Well Arnold Matthews told lies. He said he loved you better than Edith, and he whispered behind your back to her.'

'I swear I didn't, Patricia, I don't love Edith at all!'

Patricia stopped walking. 'You don't love Edith?'

'No, I've told you, it's you. I don't love her at all,' he said. 'Oh! my God, what a day! Don't you believe me? It's you, Patricia. Edith isn't anything. I just used to meet her; I'm always in the park.'

'But you told her you loved her.'

The boy stood bewildered between them. Why was Patricia so angry and serious? Her face was flushed and her eyes shone. Her chest moved up and down. He saw the long black hairs on her leg through a tear in her stockings. Her leg is as big as my middle, he thought. I'm cold; I want tea; I've got snow in my fly.

Arnold backed slowly down the path. 'I had to tell her that or she wouldn't have gone away. I had to, Patricia. You saw what she was like. I hate her. Cross my heart!'

'Bang! bang!' cried the boy.

Patricia was smacking Arnold, tugging at his muffler, knocking him with her elbows. She pummelled him down the path, and shouted at the top of her voice: 'I'll teach you to lie to Edith! You pig! you black! I'll teach you to break her heart!'

He shielded his face from her blows as he staggered back. 'Patricia, Patricia, don't hit me! There's people!'

As Arnold fell, two women with umbrellas up peered through the whirling snow from behind a bush.

Patricia stood over him. 'You lied to her and you'd lie to me,' she said. 'Get up, Arnold Matthews!'

He rose and set his muffler straight and wiped his eyes with the red handkerchief, and raised his cap and walked towards the shelter.

'And as for you,' Patricia said, turning to the watching women, 'you should be ashamed of yourselves! Two old women playing about in the snow.'

They dodged behind the bush.

Patricia and the boy climbed, hand in hand, back to the upper walk.

'I've left my cap by the snowman,' he remembered. 'It's my cap with the Tottenham colours.'

'Run back quickly,' she said, 'you can't get any wetter than you are.'

He found his cap half hidden under snow. In a corner of the shelter, Arnold sat reading the letters that Edith had dropped, turning the wet pages slowly. He did not see the boy, and the boy, behind a pillar, did not interrupt him. Arnold read every letter carefully.

'You've been a long time finding your cap,' Patricia said. 'Did you see the young man?'

'No,' he said, 'he was gone.'

At home, in the warm living-room, Patricia made him change his clothes again. He held his hands in front of the fire, and soon they began to hurt.

'My hands are on fire,' he told her, 'and my toes, and my face.'

After she had comforted him, she said: 'There, that's better. The hurting's gone. You won't call the king your uncle in a minute.' She was bustling about the room. 'Now we've all had a good cry today.'

EXTRAORDINARY LITTLE COUGH

ONE AFTERNOON, in a particularly bright and glowing August, some years before I knew I was happy, George Hooping, whom we called Little Cough, Sidney Evans, Dan Davies, and I sat on the roof of a lorry travelling to the end of the Peninsula. It was a tall, six-wheeled lorry, from which we could spit on the roofs of the passing cars and throw our apple stumps at women on the pavement. One stump caught a man on a bicycle in the middle of the back, he swerved across the road, for a moment we sat quiet and George Hooping's face grew pale. And if the lorry runs over him, I thought calmly as the man on the bicycle swayed towards the hedge, he'll get killed and I'll be sick on my trousers and perhaps on Sidney's too, and we'll be arrested and hanged, except George Hooping who didn't have an apple.

But the lorry swept past; behind us, the bicycle drove into the hedge, the man stood up and waved his fist, and I waved my cap back at him.

'You shouldn't have waved your cap,' said Sidney Evans, 'he'll know what school we're in.' He was clever, dark, and careful, and had a purse and a wallet.

'We're not in school now.'

'Nobody can expel me,' said Dan Davies. He was leaving next term to serve in his father's fruit shop for a salary.

We all wore haversacks, except George Hooping whose mother had given him a brown-paper parcel that kept coming undone, and carried a suitcase each. I had placed a coat over my suitcase because the initials on it were 'N.T.' and everybody would know that it belonged to my sister. Inside the lorry were two tents, a box of food, a packing-case of kettles and saucepans and knives and forks, an oil lamp, a primus stove, groundsheets and blankets, a gramophone with three records, and a tablecloth from George Hooping's mother.

We were going to camp for a fortnight in Rhossilli, in a field above the sweeping five-mile beach. Sidney and Dan had stayed there last year, coming back brown and swearing, full of stories of campers' dances round the fires at midnight, and elderly girls from the training college who sun-bathed naked on ledges of rocks surrounded by laughing boys, and singing in bed that lasted until dawn. But George had never left home for more than a night; and then, he told me one half-holiday when it was raining and there was nothing to do but stay in the wash-house racing his guinea-pigs giddily along the benches, it was only to stay in St Thomas, three miles from his house, with an aunt who could see through the walls and who knew what a Mrs Hoskin was doing in the kitchen.

'How much further?' asked George Hooping, clinging to his split parcel, trying in secret to push back socks and suspenders, enviously watching the solid green fields skim by as though the roof were a raft on an ocean with a motor in it. Anything upset his stomach, even liquorice and sherbet, but I alone knew that he wore long combinations in the summer with his name stitched in red on them.

'Miles and miles,' Dan said.

'Thousands of miles,' I said. 'It's Rhossilli, U.S.A. We're going to camp on a bit of rock that wobbles in the wind.'

'And we have to tie the rock on to a tree.'

'Cough can use his suspenders,' Sidney said.

The lorry roared round a corner – 'Upsy-daisy! Did you feel it then, Cough? It was on one wheel' – and below us, beyond fields and farms, the sea, with a steamer puffing on its far edge, shimmered.

'Do you see the sea down there, it's shimmering, Dan,' I said.

George Hooping pretended to forget the lurch of the slippery roof and, from that height, the frightening smallness of the sea.

Gripping the rail of the roof, he said: 'My father saw a killer whale.' The conviction in his voice died quickly as he began. He beat against the wind with his cracked, treble voice, trying to make us believe. I knew he wanted to find a boast so big it would make our hair stand up and stop the wild lorry.

'Your father's a herbalist.' But the smoke on the horizon was the white, curling fountain the whale blew through his nose, and its black nose was the bow of the poking ship.

'Where did he keep it, Cough, in the wash-house?'

'He saw it in Madagascar. It had tusks as long as from here to, from here to . . .'

'From here to Madagascar.'

All at once the threat of a steep hill disturbed him. No longer bothered about the adventures of his father, a small, dusty, skull-capped and alpaca-coated man standing and mumbling all day in a shop full of herbs and curtained holes in the wall, where old men with backache and young girls in trouble waited for consultations in the half-dark, he stared at the hill swooping up and clung to Dan and me.

'She's doing fifty!'

'The brakes have gone, Cough!'

He twisted away from us, caught hard with both hands on the rail, pulled and trembled, pressed on a case behind him with his foot, and steered the lorry to safety round a stone-walled corner and up a gentler hill to a gate of a battered farm-house.

Leading down from the gate, there was a lane to the first beach. It was high tide, and we heard the sea dashing. Four boys on a roof – one tall, dark, regular-featured, precise of speech, in a good suit, a boy of the world; one squat, ungainly, red-haired, his red wrists fighting out of short, frayed sleeves; one heavily spectacled, small-paunched, with indoor shoulders and feet in always unlaced boots wanting to go different ways; one small, thin, indecisively active, quick to get dirty, curly – saw their field in front of them, a fortnight's new home that had thick, pricking hedges for walls, the sea for a front garden, a green gutter for a lavatory, and a wind-struck tree in the very middle.

I helped Dan unload the lorry while Sidney tipped the driver and George struggled with the farm-yard gate and looked at the ducks inside. The lorry drove away.

'Let's build our tents by the tree in the middle,' said George.

'Pitch!' Sidney said, unlatching the gate for him.

We pitched our tents in a corner, out of the wind.

'One of us must light the primus,' Sidney said, and, after George had burned his hand, we sat in a circle outside the sleeping-tent talking about motor-cars, content to be in the country, lazily easy in each other's company, thinking to ourselves as we talked, knowing always that the sea dashed on the rocks not far below us and rolled out into the world, and that tomorrow we would bathe and throw a ball on the sands and stone a bottle on a rock and perhaps meet three girls. The oldest would be for Sidney, the plainest for Dan, and the youngest for me. George broke his spectacles when he spoke to girls; he had to walk off, blind as a bat, and the next morning he would say: 'I'm sorry I had to leave you, but I remembered a message.'

It was past five o'clock. My father and mother would have finished tea; the plates with famous castles on them were cleared from the table; father with a newspaper, mother with socks, were far away in the blue haze to the left, up a hill, in a villa, hearing from the park the faint cries of children drift over the public tennis court, and wondering where I was and what I was doing. I was alone with my friends in a field, with a blade of grass in my mouth saying 'Dempsey would hit him cold,' and thinking of the great whale that George's father never saw thrashing on the top of the sea, or plunging underneath, like a mountain.

'Bet you I can beat you to the end of the field.'

Dan and I raced among the cowpats, George thumping at our heels.

'Let's go down to the beach.'

Sidney led the way, running straight as a soldier in his khaki shorts, over a stile, down fields to another, into a wooded valley, up through heather on to a clearing near the edge of the cliff, where two broad boys were wrestling outside a tent. I saw one bite the other in the leg, they both struck expertly and savagely at the face, one struggled clear, and, with a leap, the other had him face to the ground. They were Brazell and Skully.

'Hallo, Brazell and Skully!' said Dan.

Skully had Brazell's arm in a policeman's grip; he gave it two quick twists and stood up, smiling.

'Hallo, boys! Hallo, Little Cough! How's your father?'

'He's very well, thank you.'

Brazell, on the grass, felt for broken bones. 'Hallo, boys! How are your fathers?'

They were the worst and biggest boys in school. Every day for a term they caught me before class began and wedged me in the waste-paper basket and then put the basket on the master's desk. Sometimes I could get out and sometimes not. Brazell was lean, Skully was fat.

'We're camping in Button's field,' said Sidney.

'We're taking a rest cure here,' said Brazell. 'And how is Little Cough these days? Father given him a pill?'

We wanted to run down to the beach, Dan and Sidney and George and I, to be alone together, to walk and shout by the sea in the country, throw stones at the waves, remember adventures and make more to remember.

'We'll come down to the beach with you,' said Skully.

He linked arms with Brazell, and they strolled behind us, imitating George's wayward walk and slashing the grass with switches.

Dan said hopefully: 'Are you camping here for long, Brazell and Skully?'

'For a whole nice fortnight, Davies and Thomas and Evans and Hooping.'

When we reached Mewslade beach and flung ourselves down, as I scooped up sand and it trickled, grain by grain through my fingers, as George peered at the sea through his double lenses and Sidney and Dan heaped sand over his legs, Brazell and Skully sat behind us like two warders.

'We thought of going to Nice for a fortnight,' said Brazell – he rhymed it with ice, dug Skully in the ribs – 'but the air's nicer here for the complexion.'

'It's as good as a herb,' said Skully.

They shared an enormous joke, cuffing and biting and wrestling again, scattering sand in the eyes, until they fell back with laughter, and Brazell wiped the blood from his nose with a piece of picnic paper. George lay covered to the waist in sand. I watched the sea slipping out, with birds quarrelling over it, and the sun beginning to go down patiently.

'Look at Little Cough,' said Brazell. 'Isn't he extraordinary? He's growing out of the sand. Little Cough hasn't got any legs.'

'Poor Little Cough,' said Skully, 'he's the most extraordinary boy in the world.'

'Extraordinary Little Cough,' they said together, 'extraordinary, extraordinary, extraordinary.' They made a song out of it, and both conducted with their switches.

'He can't swim.'

'He can't run.'

'He can't learn.'

'He can't bowl.'

'He can't bat.'

'And I bet he can't make water.'

George kicked the sand from his legs. 'Yes, I can!'

'Can you swim?'

'Can you run?'

'Can you bowl?'

'Leave him alone,' Dan said.

They shuffled nearer to us. The sea was racing out now. Brazell said in a serious voice, wagging his finger: 'Now, quite truthfully, Cough, aren't you extraordinary? Very extraordinary? Say "Yes" or "No."'

'Categorically, "Yes" or "No."' said Skully.

'No,' George said. 'I can swim and I can run and I can play cricket. I'm not frightened of anybody.'

I said: 'He was second in the form last term.'

'Now isn't that extraordinary? If he can be second he can be first. But no, that's too ordinary. Little Cough must be second.'

'The question is answered,' said Skully. 'Little Cough is extraordinary.' They began to sing again.

'He's a very good runner,' Dan said.

'Well, let him prove it. Skully and I ran the whole length of Rhossilli sands this morning, didn't we, Skull?'

'Every inch.'

'Can Little Cough do it?'

'Yes,' said George.

'Do it, then.'

'I don't want to.'

'Extraordinary Little Cough can't run,' they sang, 'can't run, can't run.'

Three girls, all fair, came down the cliff-side arm in arm, dressed in short, white trousers. Their arms and legs and throats were brown as berries; I could see when they laughed that their teeth were very white; they stepped on to the beach, and Brazell and Skully stopped singing. Sidney smoothed his hair back, rose casually, put his hands in his pockets, and walked towards the girls, who now stood close together, gold and brown, admiring the sunset with little attention, patting their scarves, turning smiles on each other. He stood in front of them, grinned, and saluted: 'Hallo, Gwyneth! do you remember me?'

'La-di-da!' whispered Dan at my side, and made a mock salute to George still peering at the retreating sea.

'Well, if this isn't a surprise!' said the tallest girl. With little studied movements of her hands, as though she were distributing flowers, she introduced Peggy and Jean.

Fat Peggy, I thought, too jolly for me, with hockey legs and tomboy crop, was the girl for Dan; Sidney's Gwyneth was a distinguished piece and quite sixteen, as immaculate and unapproachable as a girl in Ben Evans's stores; but Jean, shy and curly, with butter-coloured hair, was mine. Dan and I walked slowly to the girls.

I made up two remarks: 'Fair's fair, Sidney, no bigamy abroad,' and 'Sorry we couldn't arrange to have the sea in when you came.'

Jean smiled, wriggling her heel in the sand, and I raised my cap.

'Hallo!'

The cap dropped at her feet.

As I bent down, three lumps of sugar fell from my blazer pocket. 'I've been feeding a horse,' I said, and began to blush guiltily when all the girls laughed.

I could have swept the ground with my cap, kissed my hand gaily, called them señoritas, and made them smile without tolerance. Or I could have stayed at a distance, and this would have been better still, my hair blown in the wind, though there was no wind at all that evening, wrapped in mystery and staring at the sun, too aloof to speak to girls; but I knew that all the time my ears would have been burning, my stomach would have been as hollow and as full of voices as a shell. 'Speak to them quickly, before they go away!' a voice would have said insistently over the dramatic silence, as I stood like Valentino on the edge of the bright, invisible bull-ring of the sands. 'Isn't it lovely here!' I said.

I spoke to Jean alone; and this is love, I thought, as she nodded her head and swung her curls and said: 'It's nicer than Porthcawl.'

Brazell and Skully were two big bullies in a nightmare; I forgot them when Jean and I walked up the cliff, and looking back to see if they were baiting George again or wrestling together, I saw that George had disappeared around the corner of the rocks and that they were talking at the foot of the cliff with Sidney and the two girls.

'What's your name?'

I told her.

'That's Welsh,' she said.

'You've got a beautiful name.'

'Oh, it's just ordinary.'

'Shall I see you again?'

'If you want to.'

'I want to all right! We can go and bathe in the morning. And we can try to get an eagle's egg. Did you know that there were eagles here?'

'No,' she said. 'Who was that handsome boy on the beach, the tall one with dirty trousers?'

'He's not handsome, that's Brazell. He never washes or combs his hair or anything. He's a bully and he cheats.'

'I think he's handsome.'

We walked into Button's field, and I showed her inside the tents and gave her one of George's apples. 'I'd like a cigarette,' she said.

It was nearly dark when the others came. Brazell and Skully were with Gwyneth, one each side of her holding her arms, Sidney was with Peggy, and Dan walked, whistling, behind with his hands in his pockets.

'There's a pair,' said Brazell, 'they've been here all alone and they aren't even holding hands. You want a pill,' he said to me.

'Build Britain's babies,' said Skully.

'Go on!' Gwyneth said. She pushed him away from her, but she was laughing, and she said nothing when he put his arm around her waist.

'What about a bit of fire?' said Brazell.

Jean clapped her hands like an actress. Although I knew I loved her, I didn't like anything she said or did.

'Who's going to make it?'

'He's the best, I'm sure,' she said, pointing at me.

Dan and I collected sticks, and by the time it was quite dark there was a fire crackling. Inside the sleeping-tent, Brazell and Jean sat close together; her golden head was on his shoulder;

Skully, near them, whispered to Gwyneth; Sidney unhappily held Peggy's hand.

'Did you ever see such a sloppy lot?' I said, watching Jean smile in the fiery dark.

'Kiss me, Charley!' said Dan.

We sat by the fire in the corner of the field. The sea, far out, was still making a noise. We heard a few nightbirds. '"Tu-whit! tu-whoo!" Listen! I don't like owls,' Dan said, 'they scratch your eyes out!' – and tried not to listen to the soft voices in the tent. Gwyneth's laughter floated out over the suddenly moonlit field, but Jean, with the beast, was smiling and silent in the covered warmth; I knew her little hand was in Brazell's hand.

'Women!' I said.

Dan spat in the fire.

We were old and alone, sitting beyond desire in the middle of the night, when George appeared, like a ghost, in the fire-light and stood there trembling until I said: 'Where've you been? You've been gone hours. Why are you trembling like that?'

Brazell and Skully poked their heads out.

'Hallo, Cough my boy! How's your father? What have you been up to tonight?'

George Hooping could hardly stand. I put my hand on his shoulder to steady him, but he pushed it away.

'I've been running on Rhossilli sands! I ran every bit of it! You said I couldn't, and I did! I've been running and running!'

Someone inside the tent had put a record on the gramophone. It was a selection from *No, No, Nanette*.

'You've been running all the time in the dark, Little Cough?'

'And I bet I ran it quicker than you did, too!' George said.

'I bet you did,' said Brazell.

'Do you think we'd run five miles?' said Skully.

Now the tune was 'Tea for Two.'

'Did you ever hear anything so extraordinary? I told you

Cough was extraordinary. Little Cough's been running all night.'

'Extraordinary, extraordinary, extraordinary Little Cough,' they said.

Laughing from the shelter of the tent into the darkness, they looked like a boy with two heads. And when I stared round at George again he was lying on his back fast asleep in the deep grass and his hair was touching the flames.

THE FOLLOWERS

IT WAS six o'clock on a winter's evening. Thin, dingy rain spat and drizzled past the lighted street lamps. The pavements shone long and yellow. In squeaking goloshes, with mackintosh collars up and bowlers and trilbies weeping, youngish men from the offices bundled home against the thistly wind —

'Night, Mr Macey.'

'Going my way, Charlie?'

'Ooh, there's a pig of a night!'

'Good night, Mr Swan' —

and older men, clinging on to the big, black circular birds of their umbrellas, were wafted back, up the gaslit hills, to safe, hot, slippered, weatherproof hearths, and wives called Mother, and old, fond, fleabag dogs, and the wireless babbling.

Young women from the offices, who smelt of scent and powder and wet pixie hoods and hair, scuttled, giggling, arm-in-arm, after the hissing trams, and screeched as they splashed their stockings in the puddles rainbowed with oil between the slippery lines.

In a shop window, two girls undressed the dummies:

'Where you going tonight?'

'Depends on Arthur. Up she comes.'

'Mind her cami-knicks, Edna . . .'

The blinds came down over another window.

A newsboy stood in a doorway, calling the news to nobody, very softly:

'Earthquake. Earthquake in Japan.'

Water from a chute dripped on to his sacking. He waited in his own pool of rain.

A flat, long girl drifted, snivelling into her hanky, out of a jeweller's shop, and slowly pulled the steel shutters down with a hooked pole. She looked, in the grey rain, as though she were crying from top to toe.

A silent man and woman, dressed in black, carried the wreaths away from the front of their flower shop into the scented deadly darkness behind the window lights. Then the lights went out.

A man with a balloon tied to his cap pushed a shrouded barrow up a dead end.

A baby with an ancient face sat in its pram outside the wine vaults, quiet, very wet, peering cautiously all round it.

It was the saddest evening I had ever known.

A young man, with his arm round his girl, passed by me, laughing; and she laughed back, right into his handsome, nasty face. That made the evening sadder still.

I met Leslie at the corner of Crimea Street. We were both about the same age: too young and too old. Leslie carried a rolled umbrella, which he never used, though sometimes he pressed doorbells with it. He was trying to grow a moustache. I wore a check, ratting cap at a Saturday angle. We greeted each other formally:

'Good evening, old man.'

'Evening, Leslie.'

'Right on the dot, boy.'

A plump, blonde girl, smelling of wet rabbits, self-conscious even in that dirty night, minced past on high-heeled shoes. The heels clicked, the soles squelched.

Leslie whistled after her, low and admiring.

'Business first,' I said.

'Oh, boy!' Leslie said.

'And she's too fat as well.'

'I like them corpulent,' Leslie said. 'Remember Penelope Bogan? a Mrs too.'

'Oh, come *on*. That old bird of Paradise Alley! How's the exchequer, Les?'

'One and a penny. How you fixed?'

'Tanner.'

'What'll it be, then? The Compasses?'

'Free cheese at the Marlborough.'

We walked towards the Marlborough, dodging umbrella spokes, smacked by our windy macs, stained by steaming lamp-light, seeing the sodden, blown scourings and street-wash of the town, papers, rags, dregs, rinds, fag-ends, balls of fur, flap, float, and cringe along the gutters, hearing the sneeze and rattle of the bony trams and a ship hoot like a fog-ditched owl in the bay, and Leslie said:

'What'll we do after?'

'We'll follow someone,' I said.

'Remember following the old girl up Kitchener Street? The one who dropped her handbag?'

'You should have given it back.'

'There wasn't anything in it, only a piece of bread-and-jam.'

'Here we are,' I said.

The Marlborough saloon was cold and empty. There were notices on the damp walls: No Singing. No Dancing. No Gambling. No Peddlers.

'You sing,' I said to Leslie, 'and I'll dance, then we'll have a game of nap and I'll peddle my braces.'

The barmaid, with gold hair and two gold teeth in front, like a well-off rabbit's, was blowing on her nails and polishing them on her black marocain. She looked up as we came in, then blew on her nails again and polished them without hope.

'You can tell it isn't Saturday night,' I said. 'Evening, Miss. Two pints.'

'And a pound from the till,' Leslie said.

'Give us your one-and-a-penny, Les,' I whispered, and then said aloud: 'Anybody can tell it isn't Saturday night. Nobody sick.'

'Nobody here to *be* sick,' Leslie said.

The peeling, liver-coloured room might never have been drunk in at all. Here, commercials told jokes and had Scotches and sodas with happy, dyed, port-and-lemon women; dejected regulars grew grand and muzzy in the corners, inventing their pasts, being rich, important, and loved; reprobate grannies in dustbin black cackled and nipped; influential nobodies revised the earth; a party, with earrings, called 'Frilly Willy' played the crippled piano, which sounded like a hurdy-gurdy playing under water, until the publican's nosy wife said, 'No.' Strangers came and went, but mostly went. Men from the valleys dropped in for nine or ten; sometimes there were fights; and always there was something doing, some argie-bargie, giggle and bluster, horror or folly, affection, explosion, nonsense, peace, some wild-goose flying in the boozy air of that comfortless, humdrum nowhere in the dizzy, ditchwater town at the end of the railway lines. But that evening it was the saddest room I had ever known.

Leslie said, in a low voice: 'Think she'll let us have one on tick?'

'Wait a bit, boy,' I murmured. 'Wait for her to thaw.'

But the barmaid heard me, and looked up. She looked clean through me, back through my small history to the bed I was born in, then shook her gold head.

'I don't know what it is,' said Leslie as we walked up Crimea Street in the rain, 'but I feel kind of depressed tonight.'

'It's the saddest night in the world,' I said.

We stopped, soaked and alone, to look at the stills outside the cinema we called the Itch-pit. Week after week, for years and years, we had sat on the edges of the springless seats there, in the dank but snug, flickering dark, first with toffees and monkey-nuts that crackled for the dumb guns, and then with cigarettes: a cheap special kind that would make a fire-swallower cough up the cinders of his heart. 'Let's go in and see Lon Chaney,' I said, 'and Richard Talmadge and Milton Sills and . . . and Noah Beary,' I said, 'and Richard Dix . . . and Slim Summerville and Hoot Gibson.'

We both sighed.

'Oh, for our vanished youth,' I said.

We walked on heavily, with wilful feet, splashing the passers-by.

'Why don't you open your brolly?' I said.

'It won't open. You try.'

We both tried, and the umbrella suddenly bellied out, the spokes tore through the soaking cover; the wind danced its tatters; it wrangled above us in the wind like a ruined, mathematical bird. We tried to tug it down: an unseen, new spoke sprang through its ragged ribs. Leslie dragged it behind him, along the pavement, as though he had shot it.

A girl called Dulcie, scurrying to the Itch-pit, sniggered 'Hallo,' and we stopped her.

'A rather terrible thing has happened,' I said to her. She was so silly that, even when she was fifteen, we had told her to eat soap to make her straw hair crinkle, and Les took a piece from the bathroom, and she did.

'I know,' she said, 'you broke your gamp.'

'No, you're wrong there,' Leslie said. 'It isn't *our* umbrella at all. It fell off the roof. *You* feel,' he said. 'You can feel it fell off the roof.' She took the umbrella gingerly by its handle.

'There's someone up there throwing umbrellas down,' I said. 'It may be serious.'

She began to titter, and then grew silent and anxious as Leslie said: 'You never know. It might be walking-sticks next.'

'Or sewing-machines,' I said.

'You wait here, Dulce, and we'll investigate,' Leslie said.

We hurried on down the street, turned a blowing corner, and then ran.

Outside Rabiotti's café, Leslie said: 'It isn't fair on Dulcie.' We never mentioned it again.

A wet girl brushed by. Without a word, we followed her. She cantered, long-legged, down Inkerman Street and through Paradise Passage, and we were at her heels.

'I wonder what's the point in following people,' Leslie said, 'it's kind of daft. It never gets you anywhere. All you do is follow them home and then try to look through the window and see what they're doing and mostly there's curtains anyway. I bet nobody else does things like that.'

'You never know,' I said. The girl turned into St Augustus Crescent, which was a wide lamplit mist. 'People are always following people. What shall we call her?'

'Hermione Weatherby,' Leslie said. He was never wrong about names. Hermione was fey and stringy, and walked like a long gym-mistress, full of love, through the stinging rain.

'You never know. You never know what you'll find out. Perhaps she lives in a huge house with all her sisters —'

'How many?'

'Seven. All full of love. And when she gets home they all change into kimonos and lie on divans with music and whisper to each other and all they're doing is waiting for somebody like us to walk in, lost, and then they'll all chatter round us like starlings and put us in kimonos too, and we'll never leave the house until we die. Perhaps it's so beautiful and soft and noisy – like a warm bath full of birds . . .'

'I don't want birds in my bath,' said Leslie. 'Perhaps she'll slit her throat if they don't draw the blinds. I don't care what happens so long as it's interesting.'

She slip-slopped round a corner into an avenue where the neat trees were sighing and the cosy windows shone.

'I don't want old feathers in the tub,' Leslie said.

Hermione turned in at number thirteen, Beach-view.

'You can see the beach all right,' Leslie said, 'if you got a periscope.'

We waited on the pavement opposite, under a bubbling lamp, as Hermione opened her door, and then we tiptoed across and down the gravel path and were at the back of the house, outside an uncurtained window.

Hermione's mother, a round, friendly, owlish woman in a pinafore, was shaking a chip-pan on the kitchen stove.

'I'm hungry,' I said.

'Ssh!'

We edged to the side of the window as Hermione came into the kitchen. She was old, nearly thirty, with a mouse-brown shingle and big earnest eyes. She wore horn-rimmed spectacles and a sensible, tweed costume, and a white shirt with a trim bow-tie. She looked as though she tried to look like a secretary in domestic films, who had only to remove her spectacles and have her hair cherished, and be dressed like a silk dog's dinner, to turn into a dazzler and make her employer Warner Baxter, gasp, woo, and marry her; but if Hermione took off her glasses, she wouldn't be able to tell if he was Warner Baxter or the man who read the meters.

We stood so near the window, we could hear the chips spitting.

'Have a nice day in the office, dear? There's weather,' Hermione's mother said, worrying the chip-pan.

'What's *her* name, Les?'

'Hetty.'

Everything there in the warm kitchen, from the tea-caddy and the grandmother clock, to the tabby that purred like a kettle, was good, dull, and sufficient.

'Mr Trustcott was something awful,' Hermione said as she put on slippers.

'Where's her kimono?' Leslie said.

'Here's a nice cup of tea,' said Hetty.

'Everything's nice in that old hole,' said Leslie, grumbling. 'Where's the seven sisters like starlings?'

It began to rain much more heavily. It bucketed down on the black back yard, and the little comfy kennel of a house, and us, and the hidden, hushed town, where, even now, in the haven of the Marlborough, the submarine piano would be tinning 'Daisy', and the happy henna'd women squealing into their port.

Hetty and Hermione had their supper. Two drowned boys watched them enviously.

'Put a drop of Worcester on the chips,' Leslie whispered; and by God she did.

'Doesn't anything happen anywhere?' I said, 'in the whole wide world? I think the *News of the World* is all made up. Nobody murders no one. There isn't any sin any more, or love, or death, or pearls and divorces and mink-coats or anything, or putting arsenic in the cocoa . . .'

'Why don't they put on some music for us,' Leslie said, 'and do a dance? It isn't every night they got two fellows watching them in the rain. Not *every* night, anyway!'

All over the dripping town, small lost people with nowhere to go and nothing to spend were gooseberrying in the rain outside wet windows, but nothing happened.

'I'm getting pneumonia,' Leslie said.

The cat and the fire were purring, grandmother time ticktocked our lives away. The supper was cleared, and Hetty and Hermione, who had not spoken for many minutes, they were so confident and close in their little lighted box, looked at one another and slowly smiled.

They stood still in the decent, purring kitchen, facing one another.

'There's something funny going to happen,' I whispered very softly.

'It's going to begin,' Leslie said.

We did not notice the sour, racing rain any more.

The smiles stayed on the faces of the two still, silent women.

'It's going to begin.'

And we heard Hetty say in a small secret voice: 'Bring out the album, dear.'

Hermione opened a cupboard and brought out a big, stiff-coloured photograph album, and put it in the middle of the table. Then she and Hetty sat down at the table, side by side, and Hermione opened the album.

'That's Uncle Eliot who died in Porthcawl, the one who had the cramp,' said Hetty.

They looked with affection at Uncle Eliot, but we could not see him.

'That's Martha-the-woolshop, you wouldn't remember her, dear, it was wool, wool, wool, with her all the time; she wanted to be buried in her jumper, the mauve one, but her husband put his foot down. He'd been in India. That's your Uncle Morgan,' Hetty said, 'one of the Kidwelly Morgans, remember him in the snow?'

Hermione turned a page. 'And that's Myfanwy, she got queer all of a sudden, remember. It was when she was milking. That's your cousin Jim, the Minister, until they found out. And that's our Beryl,' Hetty said.

But she spoke all the time like somebody repeating a lesson: a well-loved lesson she knew by heart.

We knew that she and Hermione were only waiting.

Then Hermione turned another page. And we knew, by their secret smiles, that this was what they had been waiting for.

'My sister Katinka,' Hetty said.

'Auntie Katinka,' Hermione said. They bent over the photograph.

'Remember that day in Aberystwyth, Katinka?' Hetty said softly. 'The day we went on the choir outing.'

'I wore my new white dress,' a new voice said.

Leslie clutched at my hand.

'And a straw hat with birds,' said the clear, new voice.

Hermione and Hetty were not moving their lips.

'I was always a one for birds on my hat. Just the plumes of course. It was August the third, and I was twenty-three.'

'Twenty-three come October, Katinka,' Hetty said.

'That's right, love,' the voice said. 'Scorpio I was. And we met Douglas Pugh on the Prom and he said: "You look like a queen today, Katinka," he said. "You look like a queen, Katinka," he said. Why are those two boys looking in at the window?'

We ran up the gravel drive, and around the corner of the house, and into the avenue and out on to St Augustus Crescent.

The rain roared down to drown the town. There we stopped for breath. We did not speak or look at each other. Then we walked on through the rain. At Victoria corner, we stopped again.

'Good night, old man,' Leslie said.

'Good night,' I said.

And we went our different ways.

AFTER THE FAIR

THE FAIR was over, the lights in the coconut stalls were put out, and the wooden horses stood still in the darkness, waiting for the music and the hum of the machines that would set them trotting forward. One by one, in every booth, the naphtha jets were turned down and the canvases pulled over the little gaming tables. The crowd went home, and there were lights in the windows of the caravans.

Nobody had noticed the girl. In her black clothes she stood against the side of the roundabouts, hearing the last feet tread upon the sawdust and the last voices die in the distance. Then all alone on the deserted ground, surrounded by the shapes of wooden horses and cheap fairy boats, she looked for a place to sleep. Now here and now there, she raised the canvas that shrouded the coconut stalls and peered into the warm darkness. She was frightened to step inside, and as a mouse scampered across the littered shavings on the floor, or as the canvas creaked and a rush of wind set it dancing, she ran away and hid again near the roundabouts. Once she stepped on the boards; the bells round a horse's throat jingled and were still; she did not dare breathe again until all was quiet and the darkness had forgotten the noise of the bells. Then here and there she went peeping for a bed, into each gondola, under each tent. But there was nowhere, nowhere in all the fair for her to sleep. One place was too silent, and in another was the noise of mice. There was straw in the corner of the Astrologer's tent, but it moved as she touched it; she knelt by its side and put out her hand; she felt a baby's hand upon her own.

Now there was nowhere, so slowly she turned towards the

caravans on the outskirts of the field, and found all but two to be unlit. She waited, clutching her empty bag, and wondering which caravan she should disturb. At last she decided to knock upon the window of the little, shabby one near her, and, standing on tiptoes, she looked in. The fattest man she had ever seen was sitting in front of the stove, toasting a piece of bread. She tapped three times on the glass, then hid in the shadows. She heard him come to the top of the steps and call out 'Who? Who?' but she dare not answer. 'Who? Who?' he called again.

She laughed at his voice which was as thin as he was fat.

He heard her laughter and turned to where the darkness concealed her. 'First you tap,' he said, 'then you hide, then you laugh.'

She stepped into the circle of light, knowing she need no longer hide herself.

'A girl,' he said. 'Come in, and wipe your feet.' He did not wait but retreated into his caravan, and she could do nothing but follow him up the steps and into the crowded room. He was seated again, and toasting the same piece of bread. 'Have you come in?' he said, for his back was towards her.

'Shall I close the door?' she asked, and closed it before he replied.

She sat on the bed and watched him toast the bread until it burnt.

'I can toast better than you,' she said.

'I don't doubt it,' said the Fat Man.

She watched him put the charred toast upon a plate by his side, take another round of bread and hold that, too, in front of the stove. It burnt very quickly.

'Let me toast it for you,' she said. Ungraciously he handed her the fork and the loaf.

'Cut it,' he said, 'toast it, and eat it.'

She sat on the chair.

'See the dent you've made on my bed,' said the Fat Man. 'Who are you to come in and dent my bed?'

'My name is Annie,' she told him.

Soon all the bread was toasted and buttered, so she put it in the centre of the table and arranged two chairs.

'I'll have mine on the bed,' said the Fat Man. 'You'll have it here.'

When they had finished their supper, he pushed back his chair and stared at her across the table.

'I am the Fat Man,' he said. 'My home is Treorchy; the Fortune-Teller next door is Aberdare.'

'I am nothing to do with the fair,' she said, 'I am Cardiff.'

'There's a town,' agreed the Fat Man. He asked her why she had come away.

'Money,' said Annie.

Then he told her about the fair and the places he had been to and the people he had met. He told her his age and his weight and the names of his brothers and what he would call his son. He showed her a picture of Boston Harbour and the photograph of his mother who lifted weights. He told her how summer looked in Ireland.

'I've always been a fat man,' he said, 'and now I'm the Fat Man; there's nobody to touch me for fatness.' He told her of a heat-wave in Sicily and of the Mediterranean Sea. She told him of the baby in the Astrologer's tent.

'That's the stars again,' he said.

'The baby'll die,' said Annie.

He opened the door and walked out into the darkness. She looked about her but did not move, wondering if he had gone to fetch a policeman. It would never do to be caught by the policeman again. She stared through the open door into the inhospitable night and drew her chair closer to the stove.

'Better to be caught in the warmth,' she said. But she trembled at the sound of the Fat Man approaching, and pressed her hands upon her thin breast as he climbed up the steps like a walking mountain. She could see him smile through the darkness.

'See what the stars have done,' he said, and brought in the Astrologer's baby in his arms.

After she had nursed it against her and it had cried on the bosom of her dress, she told him how she had feared his going.

'What should I be doing with a policeman?'

She told him that the policeman wanted her. 'What have you done for a policeman to be wanting you?'

She did not answer but took the child nearer to her wasted breast. He saw her thinness.

'You must eat, Cardiff,' he said.

Then the child began to cry. From a little wail its voice rose into a tempest of despair. The girl rocked it to and fro on her lap, but nothing soothed it.

'Stop it! Stop it!' said the Fat Man, and the tears increased. Annie smothered it in kisses, but it howled again.

'We must do something,' she said.

'Sing it a lullaby.'

She sang, but the child did not like her singing.

'There's only one thing,' said Annie, 'we must take it on the roundabouts.' With the child's arm around her neck she stumbled down the steps and ran towards the deserted fair, the Fat Man panting behind her.

She found her way through the tents and stalls into the centre of the ground where the wooden horses stood waiting, and clambered up on to a saddle. 'Start the engine,' she called out. In the distance the Fat Man could be heard cranking up the antique machine that drove the horses all the day into a wooden gallop. She heard the spasmodic humming of the engines; the boards rattled under the horses' feet. She saw the Fat Man get up by her side, pull the central lever, and climb on to the saddle of the smallest horse of all. As the roundabout started, slowly at first and slowly gaining speed, the child at the girl's breast stopped crying and clapped its hands. The night wind tore through its hair, the music jangled in its ears. Round and round the wooden horses sped, drowning the cries of the wind with the beating of their hooves.

And so the men from the caravans found them, the Fat Man and the girl in black with a baby in her arms, racing round and round on their mechanical steeds to the ever-increasing music of the organ.

THE VISITOR

HIS HANDS were weary, though all night they had lain over
the sheets of his bed and he had moved them only to his
mouth and his wild heart. The veins ran, unhealthily blue
streams, into the white sea. Milk at his side steamed out of
a chipped cup. He smelt the morning, and knew that cocks
in the yard were putting back their heads and crowing at the
sun. What were the sheets around him if not the covering sheets
of the dead? What was the busy-voiced clock, sounding between photographs of mother and dead wife, if not the voice of
an old enemy? Time was merciful enough to let the sun shine
on his bed, and merciless to chime the sun away when night
came over and even more he needed the red light and the clear
heat.

Rhianon was attendant on a dead man, and put the chipped
edge of the cup to a dead lip. It could not be heart that beat
under the ribs. Hearts do not beat in the dead. While he had
lain ready for the inch-tape and the acid, Rhianon had cut
open his chest with a book-knife, torn out the heart, put in the
clock. He heard her say, for the third time, 'Drink the lovely
milk.' And, feeling it run sour over his tongue, and her hand
caress his forehead, he knew he was not dead. He was a living
man. For many miles the months flowed into the years, round-
ing the dry days.

Callaghan today would sit and talk with him. He heard in
his brain the voices of Callaghan and Rhianon battle until he
slept, and tasted the blood of his words. His hands were weary.
He brooded over his long, white body, marking the ribs stick
through the sides. The hands had held other hands and thrown

a ball high into the air. Now they were dead hands. He could wind them about his hair and let them rest untingling on his belly or lose them in the valley between Rhianon's breasts. It did not matter what he did with them. They were as dead as the hands of the clock, and moved to clockwork.

'Shall I close the windows until the sun's warmer?' said Rhianon.

'I'm not cold.'

He would tell her that the dead feel neither cold nor warmth, sun and wind could never penetrate his cloths. But she would laugh in her kind way and kiss him on the forehead and say to him, 'Peter, what's getting you down? You'll be out and about one day.'

One day he would walk on the Jarvis hills like a boy's ghost, and hear the people say: 'There walks the ghost of Peter, a poet, who was dead for years before they buried him.'

Rhianon tucked the sheets around his shoulders, gave him a morning kiss, and carried the chipped cup away.

A man with a brush had drawn a rib of colour under the sun and painted many circles around the circle of the sun. Death was a man with a scythe, but that summer day no living stalk was to be cut down.

The invalid waited for his visitor. Peter waited for Callaghan. His room was a world within a world. A world in him went round and round, and a sun rose in him and a moon fell. Callaghan was the west wind, and Rhianon blew away the chills of the west wind like a wind from Tahiti.

He let his hand rest on his head, stone on stone. Never had the voice of Rhianon been so remote as when it told him that the sour milk was lovely. What was she but a sweetheart talking madly to her sweetheart under a coffin of garments? Somebody in the night had turned him up and emptied him of all but a false heart. That under the ribs' armour was not his, not his the beating of a vein in the foot. His arms could no longer make their movements nor a circle around a girl to shield her from winds and robbers. There was nothing more remote under the sun than his own name, and poetry was a string of words stringed on a beanstick. With his lips he rounded a little ball of sound into some shape, and spoke a word.

There was no tomorrow for dead men. He could not think that after the next night and its sleeping, life would sprout up again like a flower through a coffin's cracks.

His room around him was a vast place. From their frames the lying likenesses of women looked down on him. That was the face of his mother, that nearly yellow oval in its frame of old gold and thinning hair. And, next to her, dead Mary. Though Callaghan blew hard, the walls around Mary would never fall down. He thought of her as she had been, remembered her Peter, darling, Peter, and her smiling eyes.

He remembered he had not smiled since that night, seven years ago, when his heart had trembled so violently within him that he had fallen to the ground. There had been strengthening in the unbelievable setting of the sun. Over the hills and the roof went the broad moons, and summer came after spring. How had he lived at all when Callaghan had not blown away the webs of the world with a great shout, and Millicent spread her loveliness about him? But the dead need no friends. He peered over the turned coffin-lid. Stiff and straight, a man of wax stared back. Taking away the pennies from those dead eyes, he looked on his own face.

'Breed, cardboard on cardboard,' he had cried, 'before I blow down your paste huts with one bellow out of my lungs.' When Mary came, there was nothing between the changing of the days but the divinity he had built around her. His child killed Mary in her womb. He felt his body turn to vapour, and men who had been light as air walked, metal-hooved, through and beyond him.

He started to cry: 'Rhianon, Rhianon, someone has upped and kicked me in the side. Drip, drip, goes my blood in me. Rhianon,' he cried.

She hurried upstairs, and time and time over again wiped away the tears from his cheeks with the sleeve of her dress.

He lay still as the morning matured and grew up into a noble noon. Rhianon passed in and out, her dress, he smelt as she bent over him, smelling of clover and milk. With a new surprise he followed her cool movements around the room, the sweep of her hands as she brushed the dead Mary in her frame. With such surprise, he thought, do the dead follow the movements of the quick, seeing the bloom under the living skin. She should be singing as she moved from mantelpiece to window, putting things right, or should be humming like a bee about her work. But if she had spoken, or laughed, or struck her nails against the thin metal of the candlesticks, drawing forth a bellnote, or if the room had been suddenly crowded with the noises of birds, he would have wept again. It pleased him to look upon the unmoving waves of the bedclothes, and think himself an island set somewhere in the south sea. Upon this island of rich and miraculous plants, the seeds grown fruits hung from the trees and, smaller than apples, dropped with the pacific winds on to the ground to lie there and be the harbourers of the summer slugs.

And thinking of the island set somewhere in the south caverns, he thought of water and longed for water. Rhianon's dress, rustling about her, made the soft noise of water. He called her over to him and touched the bosom of her dress, feeling the water on his hands. 'Water,' he told her, and told her how, as a boy, he had lain on the rocks, his fingers tracing cool shapes on the surfaces of the pools. She brought him water in a glass, and held the glass up level with his eyes so that he could see the room through a wall of water. He did not drink, and she set the glass aside. He imagined the coolness under the sea. Now, on a summer day soon after noon, he wished again for water to close utterly around him, to be no island set above the water but a green place under, staring around a dizzy cavern. He thought of some cool words, and made a line about an olive-tree that grew under a lake. But the tree was a tree of words, and the lake rhymed with another word.

'Sit and read to me, Rhianon.'

'After you have eaten,' she said, and brought him food.

He could not think that she had gone down into the kitchen and, with her own hands, prepared his meal. She had gone and had returned with food, as simply as a maiden out of the Old Testament. Her name meant nothing. It was a cool sound. She had a strange name out of the Bible. Such a woman had washed the body after it had been taken off the tree, with cool and competent fingers that touched on the holes like ten blessings. He could cry out to her: 'Put a sweet herb under my arm. With your spittle make me fragrant.'

'What shall I read you?' she asked when at last she sat by his side.

He shook his head, not caring what she read so long as he could hear her speak and think of nothing but the inflections of her voice.

'Ah! gentle may I lay me down, and gentle rest my head,
And gentle sleep the sleep of death, and gentle hear the voice
Of Him that walketh in the garden in the evening time.'

She read on until the Worm sat on the Lily's leaf.

Death lay over his limbs again, and he closed his eyes.

There was no ease from pain nor from the figures of death that went about their familiar business even in the darkness of the heavy lids.

'Shall I kiss you awake?' said Callaghan. His hand was cold on Peter's hand.

'And all the lepers kissed,' said Peter, and fell to wondering what he had meant.

Rhianon saw that he was no longer listening to her, and went on tiptoes away.

Callaghan, left alone, leant over the bed and spread the soft ends of his fingers on Peter's eyes. 'Now it is night,' he said. 'Where shall we go tonight?'

Peter opened his eyes again, saw the spreading fingers and the candles glowing like the heads of poppies. A fear and a blessing were on the room.

The candles must not be blown out, he thought. There must be light, light, light. Wick and wax must never be low. All day and all night the three candles, like three girls, must blush over my bed. These three girls must shelter me.

The first flame danced and then went out. Over the second and the third flame Callaghan pursed his grey mouth. The room was dark. 'Where shall we go tonight?' he said, but waited for no answer, pulling the sheets back from the bed and lifting Peter in his arms. His coat was damp and sweet on Peter's face.

'Oh, Callaghan, Callaghan,' said Peter with his mouth pressed on the black cloth. He felt the movements of Callaghan's body, the tense, the relaxing muscles, the curving of the shoulders, the impact of the feet on the racing earth. A wind from under the clay and the limes of the earth swept up to his hidden face. Only when the boughs of trees scraped on his back did he know that he was naked. So that he might not cry aloud, he shut his lips firmly together over a damp fold of flesh. Callaghan, too, was naked as a baby.

'Are we naked? We have our bones and our organs, our skin and our flesh. There is a ribbon of blood tied in your hair. Do not be frightened. You have a cloth of veins around your thighs.' The world charged past them, the wind dropped to nothing, blowing the fruits of battle under the moon. Peter heard the songs of birds, but no such songs as he had heard the birds, on his bedroom sill, fetch out of their throats. The birds were blind.

'Are they blind?' said Callaghan. 'They have worlds in their eyes. There is white and black in their whistling. Do not be frightened. There are bright eyes under the shells of their eggs.'

He came suddenly to a stop, Peter light as a feather in his arms, and set him gently down on a green globe of soil. Below there was a valley journeying far away with its burden of lime trees and grass into the distance where the moon hung on a navelstring from the dark. From the woods on either side came the sharp cracks of guns and the pheasants falling like a rain. But soon the night was silent, softening the triggers of the fallen twigs that had snapped out under Callaghan's feet.

Peter, conscious of his sick heart, put a hand to his side but felt none of the protecting flesh. The tips of his fingers tingled around the driving blood, but the veins were invisible. He was dead. Now he knew he was dead. The ghost of Peter, wound invisible about the ghost of the blood, stood on his globe and wondered at the corrupting night.

'What is this valley?' said Peter's voice.

'The Jarvis valley,' said Callaghan. Callaghan, too, was dead. Not a bone or a hair stood up under the steadily falling frost.

'This is no Jarvis valley.'

'This is the naked valley.'

The moon, doubling and redoubling the strength of her beams, lit up the barks and the roots and the branches of the Jarvis trees, the busy lice in the wood, the shapes of the stones and the black ants travelling under them, the pebbles in the streams, the secret grass, the untiring death-worms under the blades. From their holes in the flanks of the hills came the rats and weasels, hairs white in the moon, breeding and struggling as they rushed downward to set their teeth in the cattle's throats. No sooner did the cattle fall sucked on to the earth and the weasels race away, than all the flies, rising from the dung of the fields, came up like a fog and settled on the sides. There from the stripped valley rose the smell of death, widening the mountainous nostrils on the face of the moon. Now the sheep fell and the flies were at them. The rats and the weasels, fighting over the flesh, dropped one by one with a wound for the sheep's fleas staring out of their hair. It was to Peter but a little time before the dead, picked to the symmetrical bone, were huddled in under the soil by the wind that blew louder and harder as the fat flies dropped on to the grass. Now the worm and the death-beetle undid the fibres of the animal bones, worked at them brightly and minutely, and the weeds through the sockets and the flowers on the vanished breasts sprouted up with the colours of the dead life fresh on their leaves. And the blood that had flowed flowed over the ground, strengthening the blades of the grass, fulfilling the wind-planted seeds in its course, into the mouth of the spring. Suddenly all the streams were red with blood, a score of winding veins all over the twenty fields, thick with their clotted pebbles.

Peter, in his ghost, cried out with joy. There was life in the naked valley, life in his nakedness. He saw the streams and the beating water, how the flowers shot out of the dead, and the blades and roots were doubled in their power under the stride of the spilt blood.

And the streams stopped. Dust of the dead blew over the spring, and the mouth was choked. Dust lay over the waters like a dark ice. Light, that had been all-eyed and moving, froze in the beams of the moon.

Life in this nakedness, mocked Callaghan at his side, and Peter knew that he was pointing, with the ghost of a finger, down on to the dead streams. But as he spoke, and the shape that Peter's heart had taken in the time of the tangible flesh was aware of the knocks of terror, a life burst out of the pebbles like the thousand lives, wrapped in a boy's body, out of the womb. The streams again went on their way, and the light of the moon, in a new splendour, shone on the valley and magnified the shadows of the valley and pulled the moles and the badgers out of their winter into the deathless midnight season of the world.

'Light breaks over the hill,' said Callaghan, and lifted the invisible Peter in his arms. Dawn, indeed, was breaking far over the Jarvis wilderness still naked under the descending moon.

As Callaghan raced along the rim of the hills and into the woods and over an exultant country where the trees raced with him, Peter cried out joyfully.

He heard Callaghan's laughter like a rattle of thunder that the wind took up and doubled. There was a shouting in the wind, a commotion under the surface of the earth. Now under the roots and now on the tops of the wild trees, he and his stranger were racing against the cock. Over and under the falling fences of the light they climbed and shouted.

'Listen to the cock,' cried Peter, and the sheets of the bed rolled up to his chin.

A man with a brush had drawn a red rib down the east. The ghost of a circle around the circle of the moon spun through a cloud. He passed his tongue over his lips that had miraculously clothed themselves with skin and flesh. In his mouth was a strange taste, as if last night, three hundred nights ago, he had squeezed the head of a poppy and drunk and slept. There was the old rumour of Callaghan down his brain. From dawn to dark he had talked of death, had seen a moth caught in the candle, had heard the laughter that could not have been his ring in his ears. The cock cried again, and a bird whistled like a scythe through wheat.

Rhianon, with a sweet, naked throat, stepped into the room.

'Rhianon,' he said, 'hold my hand, Rhianon.'

She did not hear him, but stood over his bed and fixed him with an unbreakable sorrow.

'Hold my hand,' he said. And then: 'Why are you putting the sheet over my face?'

THE INTERNATIONAL EISTEDDFOD

LLANGOLLEN. A town in a vale in rolling green North Wales on a windy July morning. The sun squints out and is puffed back again into the grey clouds blowing, full to the ragged rims with rain, across the Berwyn Hills. The white-horsed River Dee hisses and paws over the hills of its stones and under the greybeard bridge. Wind smacks the river and you, it's a cold, cracking morning; birds hang and rasp over the whipped river, against their will, as though frozen still, or are wind-chaffed and scattered towards the gusty trees. As you drift down Castle Street with your hair flying, or your hat or umbrella dancing to be off and take the sky, you see and hear all about you the decorous, soberly dressed and headgeared, silent and unsmiling inhabitants of the tame town. You could be in any Welsh town on any windy snip of a morning, with only the birds and the river fuming and the only brightness the numberless greens and high purples of the hills. Everything is very ordinary in Llangollen; everything is nicely dull, except the summer world of wind and feathers, leaves and water. There is, if you are deaf, blind, and dumb, with a heart like cold bread pudding, nothing to remark or surprise. But rub your eyes with your black gloves. Here, over the bridge, come three Javanese, winged, breastplated, helmeted, carrying gongs and steel bubbles. Kilted, sporraned, tartan'd, daggered Scotsmen reel and strathspey up a side-street, piping hot. Burgundian girls, wearing, on their heads, bird-cages made of velvet, suddenly whisk on the pavement into a coloured dance. A viking goes into a pub. In black felt feathered hats and short leather trousers, enormous Austrians, with thighs big as Welshmen's bodies, but much browner, yodel to fiddles and split the rain with their smiles. Frilled, ribboned, sashed, fezzed, and white-turbaned, in baggy-blue sharavári and squashed red boots, Ukrainians with Manchester accents gopak up the hill. Everything is strange in Llangollen. You wish you had a scarlet hat, and bangles, and a little bagpipe to call your own, but it does not matter. The slapping bell-dancers, the shepherds and chamois-hunters, the fiddlers and fluters, the players on gongs and mandolines, guitars, harps, and trumpets, the beautiful flashing boys and girls of a score and more of singing countries, all the colours of the international rainbow, do not mind at all your mouse-brown moving among them: though you long, all the long Eisteddfod week, for a cloak like a blue sea or a bonfire to sweep and blaze in the wind, and a cap of bells, and a re-velling waistcoat, and a great Alp-horn to blow all over Wales from the ruins of Dinas Brân.

Now follow your nose, and the noise of guitars, and the flying hues and flourish of those big singing-birds in their clogs and aprons and bonnets, veils, flowers, more flowers, and lace, past the wee Shoppes, through the babel of the bridge, by the very white policeman conducting from a rostrum, and up the tide of the hill, past popcorn and raspberryade, to the tented Field.

Green, packed banks run, swarming, down to the huge mar-quee there that groans and strains and sings in the sudden squalls like an airship crewed full of choirs. Music spills out of the microphones all over the humming field. Out of the wind-tugged tent it rises in one voice, and the crowd outside is hushed away into Spain. In a far corner of the field, young men and women begin to dance, for every reason in the world. Out skims the sun from a cloud-shoal. The spaniel ears of the little tents flap. Children collect the autographs of Dutch farmers. You hear a hive of summer hornets: it is the Burgundian *vielle*, a mandolin with a handle. Palestrina praises from Bologna to the choral picnickers. A Breton holiday sings in the wind, to clog-tramp and *biniou*.

Here they come, to this cup and echo of hills, people who love to make music, from France, Ireland, Norway, Italy, Switzerland, Spain, Java, and Wales: fine singers and faulty, nimble dancers and rusty, pipers to make the dead swirl or chanters with crows in their throats: all countries, shapes, ages, and colours, sword-dancers, court-dancers, cross-dancers, clog-dancers, dale-dancers, morris, ceilidhe, and highland, bolero, flamenco, heel-and-toe. They love to make music move. What a rush of dancing to Llangollen's feet! And, oh, the hubbub of tongues and toes in the dark chapels where every morning there's such a shining noise as you'd think would drive the Sunday bogles out of their doldrums for ever and ever.

Inside the vast marquee that drags at its anchors, eight thousand people – and you – face a sea of flowers, begonias, magnolias, lupins, lobelias, grown for these dancing days in the gardens of the town. Banks and waves of plants and flowers flow to the stage where a company from Holland – eight married pairs of them, the oldest in their late fifties, the youngest twenty or so – are performing, in sombre black, a country dance called, 'Throw Your Wife Away'. This is followed, appropriately and a little later, by a dance called, 'You Can't Catch Me'. The movements of the humorous and simple dance are gay and sprightly. The men of the company dance like sad British railway-drivers in white clogs. Under their black, peaked caps, their faces are stern, weather-scored, and unrelenting. The quicker the music, the gloomier they clap and clog on the invisible cobbles of cold clean kitchens. The frenzied flute and fiddle whip them up into jet-black bliss as they frolic like undertakers. Long Dutch winter nights envelop them. Brueghel has painted them. They are sober as potatoes. Their lips move as they stamp and bow. Perhaps they are singing. Certainly, they are extremely happy.

And Austrians, then, to fiddles and guitar, sing a song of mowers in the Alpine meadows. Sworded Ukrainians – I mean, Ukrainians with swords – leap and kick above the planted sea. People from Tournas, in the Burgundy country, dance to accordion and *cabrette*, the Dance of the Vine – Dressers after Harvest. They plant the vines, put the leaves on the branches, hang up the grapes, pick the grapes, and press the wine. 'God gave us wine,' they sing as they dance, and the wine is poured into glasses and the dancers drink. (But the wine's not as real as the pussyfoot nudge and shudder down the aisles.)

All day the music goes on. Bell-padded, baldricked, and braided, those other foreigners, the English, dance fiercely out of the past, and some have beards, spade, gold, white, and black, to dance and wag as well.

And a chorus of Spanish ladies are sonorous and beautiful in their nighties.

And little girls from Obernkirchen sing like pigtailed angels.

All day the song and dancing in this transformed valley, this green cup of countries in the country of Wales, goes on until the sun goes in. Then, in the ship of the tent, under the wind-filled sails, watchers and listeners grow slow and close into one cloud of shadow; they gaze, from their deep lulled dark, on to the lighted deck where the country dancers weave in shifting-coloured harvests of light.

And then you climb down hill again, in a tired tide, and over the floodlit Dee to the town that won't sleep for a whole melodious week or, if it does at all, will hear all night in its sleep the hills fiddle and strum and the streets painted with tunes.

The bars are open as though they could not shut and Sunday never comes down over the fluting town like a fog or a shutter. For every reason in the world, there's a wave of dancing in the main, loud street. A fiddle at a corner tells you to dance and you do in the moon though you can't dance a step for all the Ukrainians in Llangollen. Peace plays on a concertina in the vigorous, starry street, and nobody is surprised.

When you leave the last voices and measures of the sweet-throated, waltzing streets, the lilt and ripple of the Dee leaping, and the light of the night, to lie down, and the strewn town lies down to sleep in its hills and ring of echoes, you will remember that nobody was surprised at the turn the town took and the life it danced for one week of the long, little year. The town sang and danced, as though it were right and proper as the rainbow or the rare sun to celebrate the old bright turning earth and its bullied people. Are you surprised that people still can dance and sing in a world on its head? The only surprising thing about miracles, however small, is that they sometimes happen.

PART TWO

Adventures in the Skin Trade

CHAPTER I

A FINE BEGINNING

I

THAT EARLY morning, in January 1933, only one person was awake in the street, and he was the quietest. Call him Samuel Bennet. He wore a trilby hat that had been lying by his bedside in case the two house-breakers, a man and a woman, came back for the bag they had left.

In striped pyjamas tight under the arms and torn between the legs, he padded barefoot downstairs and opened the breakfast-room door of his parents' six-room house. The room smelt strong of his father's last pipe before bed. The windows were shut fast and the curtains drawn, the back door was bolted, the house-breaking night could not enter anywhere. At first he peered uneasily into the known, flickering corners of the room, as though he feared that the family might have been sitting there in silence in the dark; then he lit the gaslight from the candle. His eyes were still heavy from a dream of untouchable city women and falling, but he could see that Tinker, the aunt-faced pom, was sleeping before the burned-out fire, and that the mantelpiece clock between hollow, mock-ebony, pawing horses, showed five to two. He stood still and listened to the noises of the house: there was nothing to fear. Upstairs the family breathed and snored securely. He heard his sister sleeping in the box-room under the signed photographs of actors from the repertory theatre and the jealous pictures of the marriages of friends. In the biggest bedroom overlooking the field that was called the back, his father turned over the bills of the month in his one dream; his mother in bed mopped and polished through a wood of kitchens. He closed the door: now there was nobody to disturb him.

But all the noises of the otherwise dead or sleeping, dark early morning, the intimate breathing of three invisible relations, the loud old dog, could wake up the neighbours. And the gaslight, bubbling, could attract to his presence in the breakfast-room at this hour Mrs Probert next door, disguised as a she-goat in a nightgown, butting the air with her kirby-grips; her dapper, commercial son, with a watch-chain tattooed across his rising belly; the tubercular lodger, with his neat umbrella up and his basin in his hand. The regular tide of the family breath could beat against the wall of the house on the other side, and bring the Baxters out. He turned the gas low and stood for a minute by the clock, listening to sleep and seeing Mrs Baxter climb naked out of her widow's bed with a mourning band round her thigh.

Soon her picture died, she crawled back grieving to her lovebird's mirror under the blankets, and the proper objects of the room slowly returned as he lost his fear that the strangers upstairs he had known since he could remember would wake and come down with pokers and candles.

First there was the long strip of snapshots of his mother propped against the cut-glass of the window-sill. A professional under a dickybird hood had snapped her as she walked down Chapel Street in December, and developed the photographs while she waited looking at the thermos flasks and the smoking sets in the nearest shop-window, calling 'Good morning' across the street to the shopping bags she knew, and the matron's outside costumes, and the hats like flower-pots and chambers on the crisp, permed heads. There she was, walking down the street along the window-sill, step by step, stout, safe, confident, buried in her errands, clutching her handbag, stepping aside from the common women blind and heavy under a week's provisions, prying into the looking-glasses at the doors of furniture shops.

'Your photograph has been taken.' Immortalized in a moment, she shopped along for ever between the cut-glass vase with the permanent flowers and the box of hairpins, buttons, screws, empty shampoo packets, cotton-reels, flypapers, cigarette cards. At nearly two in the morning she hurried down Chapel Street against a backcloth of trilbies and Burberries going the other way, umbrellas rising to the first drops of the rain a month ago, the sightless faces of people who would always be strangers hanging half-developed behind her, and the shadows of the shopping centre of the sprawling, submerged town. He could hear her shoes click on the tramrails. He could see, beneath the pastelled silk scarf, the round metal badge of Mrs Rosser's Society, and the grandmother's cameo brooch on the vee of the knitted clover jumper.

The clock chimed and struck two. Samuel put out his hand and took up the strip of snaps. Then he tore it into pieces. The whole of her dead, comfortable face remained on one piece, and he tore it across the cheeks, up through the chins, and into the eyes.

The pom growled in a nightmare, and showed his little teeth. 'Lie down, Tinker. Go to sleep, boy.' He put the pieces in his pyjama pocket.

Then there was the framed photograph of his sister by the clock. He destroyed her in one movement, and, with the ripping of her set smile and the crumpling of her bobbed head into a ball, down went the Girls' School and the long-legged, smiling colts with their black knickers and bows; the hockey-legged girls who laughed behind their hands as they came running through the gates when he passed, went torn and ruined into his pyjama pocket; they vanished, broken, into the porch and lay in pieces against his heart. Stanley Road, where the Girls' School stood, would never know him again. Down you go, Peggy, he whispered to his sister, with all the long legs and the Young Liberals' dances, and the boys you brought home for supper on Sunday evenings and Lionel you kissed in the porch. He is a solicitor now. When I was eleven years old and you were seventeen I heard you, from my bedroom, playing the Desert Song. People were downstairs all over the world.

Most of the history sheets on the table were already marked and damned in his father's violet writing. With a lump of coal from the dead fire, Samuel marked them again, rubbing the coal hard over the careful corrections, drawing legs and breasts in the margins, smudging out the names and form numbers. History is lies. Now take Queen Elizabeth. Go ahead, take Alice Phillips, take her into the shrubbery. She was the headmaster's daughter. Take old Bennet and whip him down the corridors, stuff his mouth with dates, dip his starched collar in his marking ink and hammer his teeth back into his prim, bald, boring head with his rap-across-the-knuckle ruler. Spin Mr Nicholson on his tellurion until his tail drops off. Tell Mr Parsons his wife has been seen coming out of the Compass piggyback on a drunk sailor, catching pennies in her garters. It's as true as History.

On the last sheet he signed his name several times under a giant pinman with three legs. He did not scribble on the top sheet. At a first glance there was no sign of interference. Then he threw the coal into the grate. Dust drifted up in a cloud, and settled down again on the pom's back.

If only he could shout at the ceiling now, at the dark circle made by the gas, at the cracks and lines that had always been the same faces and figures, two bearded men chasing an animal over a mountain edge, a kneeling woman with faces on her knees: Come and look at Samuel Bennet destroying his parents' house in Mortimer Street, off Stanley's Grove; he will never be allowed to come back. Mrs Baxter, have a dekko from under the cold sheets: Mr Baxter, who worked in the Harbour Trust Office, can never come back either. Mrs Probert Chestnuts, your billygoat is gone, leaving a hairy space in the bed; Mr Bell the lodger coughs all night under his gamp; your son cannot sleep, he is counting his gentlemen's three and eleven-three-half-hose jumping over the tossed blankets. Samuel shouted under his breath, 'Come and see me destroying the evidence, Mrs Rosser; have a peep from under your hairnet. I have seen your shadow on the blind as you undressed, I was watching by the lamp-post next to the dairy; you disappeared under a tent and came out slim and humped and black. I am the only gooseberry in Stanley's Grove who knows that you are a black woman with a hump. Mr Rosser married to a camel; every one is mad and bad in his box when the blinds are pulled; come and see me break the china without any noise so that I can never come back.'

'Hush,' he said to himself, 'I know you.'

He opened the door of the china pantry. The best plates shone in rows, a willow tree next to an ivied castle, baskets of solid flowers on top of fruits and flower-coiled texts. Tureens were piled on one shelf, on another the salad-bowls, the finger-bowls, the toast-racks spelling Porthcawl and Baby, the trifle-dishes, the heirloom moustache-cup. The afternoon tea-service was brittle as biscuits and had gold rims. He cracked two saucers together, and the horn-curved spout of the teapot came off in his hand. In five minutes he had broken the whole set. Let all the daughters of Mortimer Street come in and see me, he whispered in the close pantry: the pale young girls who help at home, calculating down the pavement to the rich-smelling shops, screwing up their straight, dry hair in their rooms at the top of the house; their blood is running through them like salt. And I hope the office girls knock on the door with the stubs of their fingers, rap out Sir or Madam on the glass porch, the hard, bright babies who never go too far. You can hear them in the lane behind the post office as you tiptoe along, they are saying, 'So he said and I said and he said and Oh yeah I said,' and the just male voices are agreeing softly. Shoo them in out of snoring Stanley's Grove, I know they are sleeping under the sheets up to their fringes in wishes. Beryl Gee is marrying the Chamber of Commerce in a pepper-and-salt church. Mrs Mayor's Chain, Madame Cocked Hat, Lady Settee, I am breaking tureens in the cupboard under the stairs.

A tureen-cover dropped from his hand and smashed.

He waited for the sound of his mother waking. No one stirred upstairs. 'Tinker did it,' he said aloud, but the harsh noise of his voice drove him back into silence. His fingers became so cold and numb he knew he could not lift up another plate to break it.

'What are you doing?' he said to himself at last, in a cool, flat voice. 'Leave the Street alone. Let it sleep.'

Then he closed the pantry door.

'What are you doing, ranting away?'

Even the dog had not been wakened.

'Ranting away,' he said.

He would have to be quick now. The accident in the cupboard had made him tremble so much that he could hardly tear up the bills he found in the sideboard drawer and scatter them under the sofa. His sister's crochet-work was too difficult to destroy, the doilies and the patterned tea-cosies were hard as rubber. He pulled them apart the best he could, and wedged them up the chimney.

'These are such small things,' he said. 'I should break the windows and stuff the cushions with the glass.' He saw his round soft face in the mirror under the Mona Lisa. 'But you won't,' he said, turning away; 'you're afraid of the noise.' He turned back to his reflection. 'It isn't that. You're afraid she'll cut her hands.'

He burnt the edge of his mother's sunshade at the gas-mantle, and felt the tears running down his cheeks and dropping on to his pyjama collar.

Even in the first moment of his guilt and shame, he remembered to put out his tongue and taste the track of the tears. Still crying, he said, 'It's salt. It's very salt. Just like in my poems.'

He went upstairs in the dark, with the candle shaking, past the box-room to his own room, and locked the door on the inside. He put out his hands and touched the walls and his bed. Good morning and good-bye, Mrs Baxter. His window, facing her bedroom, was open to the windless, starless early morning, but he could not hear her breathe or sleep. All the houses were quiet. The street was a close grave. The Rossers and the Proberts and the Bennets were still and safe and deep in their separate silences. His head touched the pillow, but he knew that he could not sleep again. His eyes closed.

Come down into my arms, for I shan't sleep, girls asleep on all sides in the attics and spare rooms of the square, red houses with the bay windows looking out on the trees behind the railings. I know your rooms like the backs of my hands, like the backs of your heads in the pictures when you are leaning over on to the next-door shoulders. I shan't sleep again. Tomorrow, today, I am going away by the 7.15 train, with ten pounds and a new suit-case. Lay your curling-pins on my pillow, the alarm at six-thirty will hurry you back to draw the blinds and light the fires before the rest come down. Come down quickly, the Bennets' house is melting. I can hear you breathe, I can hear Mrs Baxter turn in a dream. Oh, the milk-men are waking?

He was asleep with his hat on still, and his hands clenched.

2

THE FAMILY awoke before six o'clock. He heard them, from a sunken half-sleep, bothering on the landing. They would be in dressing-gowns, stale-eyed and with ragged hair. Peggy might have put two blushes on her cheeks. The family rushed in and out of the bathroom, never stopping to wash, and collided on the narrow top of the stairs as they nagged and bustled to get him ready. He let himself sink deeper until the waves broke round his head again, and the lights of a city spun and shone through the eyes of women walking in his last re-membered dream. From the lapping distance he heard his father shout like a man on the opposite shore:

'Have you put the sponge bag in, Hilda?'

'Of course I have,' she answered from the kitchen.

Don't let her look in the china-pantry, Samuel prayed among the women walking like lamp-posts. She never uses the best china for breakfast.

'All right, all right; I just asked.'

'Where's his new hairbrush?'

'That's right, shout my head off. Here it is. How can I give it to you if you're in the kitchen? It's the brush with the initials – S.B.'

'I know his initials.'

'Mother, does he want all these vests? You know he never uses them.'

'It's January, Peggy.'

'She knows it's January, Hilda. You haven't got to tell the neighbours. Can you smell something burning?'

'It's only mother's sunshade,' Samuel said in the locked bedroom.

He dressed and went down. The gas in the breakfast-room was on again. His mother was boiling an egg for him on the gas-stove. 'We'll have our breakfast later,' she said; 'you mustn't miss the train. Did you sleep well?'

'No burglars last night, Sam,' his father said.

His mother brought the egg in. 'You can't expect them every night.'

Peggy and his father sat down in front of the empty grate.

'What do you think you'll do first when you get there, Sam?' said Peggy.

'He'll get himself a nice room, of course, not too central. And don't have an Irish landlady.' His mother brushed his collar as he ate. 'Go and get yourself settled straight away; that's the important thing.'

'I'll get myself settled.'

'Don't forget to look under the wallpaper for bugs.'

'That's enough of that, Peggy. Sam knows a clean place when he sees one.'

He saw himself knocking at a lodging-house in the very centre of the city, and an Irishwoman appearing at the door. 'Good morning, madam. Have you a cheap room?' 'Cheaper than sunlight to you, Danny Boy.' She would not be more than twenty-one. 'Has it got bugs?' 'All over the walls, praise be to God.' 'I'll take it.'

'I'll know what I'm doing,' he said to his mother.

'Jenkins's motor isn't here yet,' Peggy said. 'Perhaps there's a puncture.'

If he doesn't come soon, they'll notice everything. I'll cut my throat on a piece of china.

'Remember to call on Mrs Chapman. Give her all our love from 42.'

'I'll call on her tomorrow, mother.'

The taxi drew up outside. The corners of bedroom blinds would be lifted all over the street.

'Here's your wallet. Don't put it in your handkerchief pocket now. You never know when you'll be wanting to blow your nose.'

'You'll be scattering largesse,' Peggy said. She kissed him on the forehead.

Remind me to wipe it off in the cab.

'You're kissing the editor of *The Times* now,' said his mother.

'Well, not quite that, Sam. Not yet, eh?' His father said, 'Rungs of the ladder,' and then looked away.

'Write tomorrow morning sharp. Send us the news.'

'You send me your news, too. Mr Jenkins is blowing his horn.'

'Better than blowing your trumpet,' Peggy said. 'And there's never any news in Mortimer Street.'

You wait, slyboots. Wait till the flames touch the doilie with the herons on it.

He came down to pat Tinker.

'Come on, don't fuss over the old dog; he's all fleas. It's gone seven.'

Peggy was opening the door of the taxi for him. His father shook him by the hand. His mother kissed him on the mouth.

'Good-bye, Mortimer Street,' he said, and the cab was off. 'Good-bye, Stanley's Grove.'

Through the back window he saw three strangers waving. He pulled down the blind.

3

Sitting with his bag in the lavatory of the moving train, for all
the compartments were full, he read through his notebook
and tore out the pages in order. He was dressed in a brand-new
brown tweed overcoat, a brown town-suit, a white starched
shirt with a woollen tie and a tiepin, and black, shining shoes.
He had put his hard brown hat in the wash-basin. Here was
Mrs Chapman's address next to the telephone number of a Mr
Hewson who was going to introduce him to a man who worked
on a newspaper; and under these the address of the Literary
Institute that had once awarded him a guinea for a poem in a
competition: Will Shakespeare at the Tomb of the Unknown
Warrior. He tore the page out. Then the name and address, in
red ink, of a collected poet who had written him a letter thank-
ing him for a sonnet-sequence. And a page of names that
might help.

The lavatory door half opened, and he shut it quickly with
his foot.

'I beg your pardon.'

Hear her apologizing down the corridor, full as an egg.
She could turn every handle the whole length of the train,
and in every closet a fully-clothed man would be sitting
with his foot against the door, lost and alone in the long,
moving house on wheels, travelling in silence with no windows, at sixty miles an hour racing to another place that did
not want him, never at home wherever the train stopped.
The handle turned again, and Samuel coughed somebody
away.

The last page of the notebook was the only one he kept.
Under a drawing of a girl with long hair dancing into an address, he had written: Lucille Harris. A man he met on the
Promenade had said as they sat on a bench, looking at the legs
passing: 'She's okay. She's a girl I know. She's the best in
the world; she'll take care of you. Give her a call when you're

up. Tell her you're Austin's friend.' That page he placed in his wallet between two one-pound notes.

The rest of the pages he picked up from the floor, bunched together, and threw down between his legs into the bowl. Then he pulled the chain. Down went the helping names, the influential numbers, the addresses that could mean so much, into the round, roaring sea and on to the rails. Already they were lost a mile behind, blowing over the track now, over the glimpses of hedges into the lightning-passing fields.

Home and help were over. He had eight pounds ten and Lucille Harris's address. Many people have begun worse, he said aloud. I am ignorant, lazy, dishonest, and sentimental; I have the pull over nobody.

The handle turned again.

'I bet you're dancing,' he said to the person the other side of the locked door.

Footsteps pattered away down the train.

First of all, when I reach there, I'll have a Bass and a stale sandwich, he decided. I'll take them to a table in a corner, brush off the cakecrumbs with my hat, and prop my book against the cruet. I must have all the details right at the beginning. The rest must come by accident. I'll be sitting there before noon, cool and calm, my hat on my knees, my glass in my hand, looking not a day under twenty, pretending to read and spying from the corners of my eyes at the waiting, drinking, restless people busily alone at the counter. The other tables will be crowded. There will be women, beckoning without moving, over their cold coffee; old, anonymous men with snuff on their cheeks, trembling over tea; quiet men expecting no one from the trains they wait for eagerly every hour; women who have come to run away, to take a train to St Ives or Liverpool or anywhere, but who know they will never take any train and are drinking cups of tea and saying to themselves, 'I could be catching the twelve o'clock but I'll wait for the quarter past'; women from the country with dozens of children coming undone; shop girls, office girls, street girls, people who have nothing worse to do, all the unhappy, happy in chains, be-wildered foreign men and women in the station buffet of the city I know from cover to cover.

The door rattled. 'You there,' a voice said outside. 'You've been there for hours.'

He turned on the hot-water tap. It spurted cold water into the basin before he could take his hat out. 'I'm a director of the company,' he said, but his voice sounded weak to him and without assurance.

When the footsteps had faded again, he gathered up his cases and walked out of the lavatory and down the corridor. Standing outside a first-class compartment, he saw a man and a ticket-inspector come to the door and hammer on it. They did not try the handle.

'Ever since Neath,' the man said.

Now the train was losing speed, running out of the lost country into the smoke and a tunnel of factories, puffing past the district platforms and the high houses with broken windows and underclothes dancing in the dirty yards. Children at the windows never waved their hands to the train. It might have been the wind passing.

A crowd of people stood arguing outside the door as the train drew up under a great glass roof.

4

'Nip of Bass, please, and a ham sandwich.' He took them to a table in a corner, brushed off the crumbs with his wet hat, and sat down just before noon. He counted his money: eight pound nine and a penny, nearly three pounds more than he had ever seen. Some people had this every week. It had to last him until he was dead. At the next table sat a plump, middle-aged man with a chocolate-brown birthmark over his cheek and chin like the half of a beard. He was propping his book against an empty bottle when a young man walked over from the counter.

'Hullo, Sam.'

'Hullo, Ron. Fancy seeing you.'

He was Ronald Bishop who used to live in the Crescent off Stanley's Grove.

'Been up in the smoke for long, Sam?'

'Just arrived. How's tricks?'

'Same as me, we must have been on the same train. Oh, so so. Still at the old game, Sam?'

'Yeah, up on a bit of business. You at the usual?'

'Yeah.'

They had never had anything to say to each other.

'Where you staying, Ron?'

'Usual. Strand Palace.'

'Dare say I'll be seeing you, then.'

'Okay, make it tomorrow in the bar, about seven-thirty.'

'Okay.'

'It's a date, don't forget.'

'No fear.'

They both forgot it at once.

'Well, be seeing you.'

'Be good.'

As Ronald Bishop walked off, Samuel said silently into his glass: A fine beginning. If I go out of the station and turn round the corner I'll be back in 42. The little Proberts will be playing doctor outside the Load of Hay. The only stranger anywhere near me is a business-man with a stained face, reading the palms of his hands. No, here comes a woman in a fur coat; she's going to sit next to me. Yes, no, no. I smelt her as she passed; eau-de-Cologne and powder and bed.

The woman sat down two tables away, crossed her legs, powdered her nose.

This is the beginning of an advance. Now she is pretending not to notice that her knees are uncovered. There's a lynx in the room, lady. Button your overcoat. She's rattling her spoon on her saucer to attract my attention, but when I stare at her hard, without smiling, I see she is looking down gently and innocently into her lap as though she had a baby there. He was glad she was not brazen.

Dear mother, he wrote with his finger on the back of an envelope, looking up, between every few invisible words, at the unnoticing woman opposite, this is to tell you that I arrived safely and that I am drinking in the buffet with a tart. I will tell you later if she is Irish. She is about thirty-eight years old and her husband left her five years ago because of her carryings on. Her child is in a home, and she visits him every other Sunday. She always tells him that she is working in a hat shop. You need not worry that she will take all my money as we liked each other on first sight. And you need not worry that I shall break my heart trying to reform her, because I have always been brought up to believe that Mortimer Street is what is right, and I would not wish that on anybody. Besides, I do not want to reform her. Not that I think she is nasty. Her business is very hard on stockings, so I am going to pay the first week's rent for our little room in Pimlico. Now she is going across to the counter to buy another cup of coffee. I hope you will notice that she is buying her own. Everybody in the buffet is unhappy except me.

As she came back to her table, he tore up the envelope and stared at her, unsmiling, for a full minute by the Bovril clock. Once she raised her eyes to his, then looked away. She was tapping her spoon on the side of her cup, then opening and closing the clasp of her handbag, then turning her head round slowly to face him and then looking away again quickly through the window. She must be new, he thought with a sudden compassion, but he did not stop staring. Should I wink? He tilted his hard, wet hat over one eye, and winked: a long, deliberate wink that screwed up his face and made his burning cigarette nearly touch the blunt end of his nose. She snapped her handbag, pushed two pennies under the saucer, and walked right out of the room, never looking at him as she passed.

She's left her coffee, he thought. And then: My God, she was blushing.

A fine beginning.

'Did you speak?' asked the man with the birthmark, spying up. His face was red and purple where it was not brown, faintly shabby and unshaved, shiftily angry about the eyes as though his cunning were an irritation impossible to bear.

'I think I said it was a fine day.'

'Stranger in town?'

'Yes, I've just come up.'

'How do you like it?' He did not appear to care at all.

'I haven't been outside the station yet.'

Now the woman in the fur coat would be telling a policeman, 'I have just been winked at by a short boy wearing a wet hat.' 'But it isn't raining, madam.' That would settle her.

He put his hat under the table.

'There's plenty to see,' the man said, 'if that's what you want. Museums, art galleries.' Without speaking, he went through a list of names of other attractions, but rejected them all. 'Museums,' he said after a long pause. 'There's one at South Kensington, and there's the British Museum, and there's one at Whitehall with guns. I've seen them all,' he said.

Now every table was occupied. Cold, stiff people with time to kill sat staring at their tea and the clock, inventing replies to questions that would not be asked, justifying their behaviour in the past and the future, drowning every present moment as soon as it began to breathe, lying and wishing, missing all the trains in the terror of their minds, each one alone at the terminus. Time was dying all over the room. And then all the tables except the one next to Samuel's were unoccupied again. The lonely crowd went out in a funeral procession, leaving ash and tea-leaves and newspapers.

'You must move out of the station some time, you know,' the man said, returning to a conversation that held no interest for him. 'If you want to see around. It's only fair. It's not fair to come up in a train and sit in the buffet and then go back and say you've seen London, is it?'

'I'm going out now, quite soon.'

'That's right,' the man said, 'give London a chance.'

He is so tired of talking to me that he is nearly losing his temper, Samuel thought.

He looked around him again, at the mourners fidgeting to the counter, at the quick whisky drinkers in a knot by the tea-urn, at the waitresses listlessly busy with cardboard cakes and small change.

'Otherwise, it's like not getting out of bed, isn't it?' the man said. 'You've got to walk round, you know, you've got to move some time. Everybody does it,' he said in a sudden, dull passion.

Samuel bought another nip of Bass from a girl like Joan Crawford.

'This is the last one, then I'm going,' he said when he had returned to his table.

'Do you think I care how many more you have? You can stay here all day, why should I mind?' The man was looking at the palms of his hands again as his temper mounted. 'Am I my brother's keeper?'

Ronald Bishop still stood at the counter.

Mortimer Street has tracked me down, Samuel thought bitterly, even into this lopsided quarrel with a palmist in a station restaurant. There was no escape. But it was not escape he wanted. The Street was a safe hole in a wall behind the wind in another country. He wanted to arrive and be caught. Ronald stood there like a fury with a rolled umbrella. Come in, Mrs Rosser, in your fawn and beige antimacassar coat, with your tribal hat on your waves, and scream the news of the Street across the table in your whist-drive voice. I could not escape your fury on a birds' rock, you would be mincing and pinching down to the fishy sea with your beak gaped open like a shopping bag.

'I hate a nosy parker,' the man said, and got up. On his way to the counter he passed the table where the Irish prostitute had sat and removed the pennies from under the plate.

'Stop, thief!' Samuel said softly. No one could hear. There is a waitress with a consumptive husband who needs those pennies. And two children, Tristram and Eve. He changed the names quickly. Tom and Marge. Then he walked over and put a sixpence under the plate just as a waitress came to the table.

'It fell on the floor,' he said.

'Oh yeah?'

As he walked back, he saw that the waitress was talking to three men at the counter and nodding her head in his direction. One man was Ronald Bishop. One was the man with the birthmark.

Oh, fine, fine! If he had not broken the china he would have caught the next train back. The pieces would be swept up by now, but the tears would be running all over the house. 'Mother, mother, he's put my crochet-work up the chimney,' he heard his sister scream in a guard's whistle. Herons, flower baskets, palm trees, windmills, Red Riding Hoods, stuffed up in the flames and soot. 'Get me a rubber to rub out coal, Hilda. I shall of course lose my position. That is only to be expected.' 'Oh my teapot, oh my blue set, oh my poor boy.' He refused to look at the counter where Ronald Bishop inaudibly reviled him. The waitress knew as soon as she saw him that he stole from the begging tins of the blind and led them by the arm into thick traffic. The birthmarked man said that he had shown a certain postcard to a customer in a fur coat. The voices of his parents condemned above the clattering of the cups. He stared hard at his book though the print climbed and staggered as if the tears of the left house had run down after him along the rails and flowed into this hot, suspicious room over the tea-stained air into his eyes. But the image was false and the book was chosen for strangers. He did not like or understand it.

'My bills.' 'My doilies.' 'My willow-plate.'

Ronald Bishop went out on to the platform.

'Be seeing you, Ron.'

Ronald Bishop's face was flushed with the embarrassment of not noticing him.

One pleasure is, Samuel said to himself, that I do not know what I expect to happen to me. He smiled at the waitress behind the counter, and she stared away at once as guiltily as though he had discovered her robbing the till. I am not so innocent as I make out, he thought. I do not expect any old cobwebbed Fagin, reeking of character and stories, to shuffle out of a corner and lead me away into his grand, loud, filthy house; there will not be any Nancy to tickle my fancy in a kitchen full of handkerchiefs and beckoning, unmade beds. I did not think a choir of loose women immediately would sing and dance around the little tables, in plush cloths and advertised brassieres, as I walked into London for the first time, rattling my fortune, fresh as Copperfield. I could count the straws in my hair with one hand.

Hush! I know you, he said, cheater at Patience, keyhole peeper, keeper of nail-clippings and ear-wax, lusting after silhouettes on Laburnum's blind, searching for thighs in the Library of Classical Favourites, Sam Thumb in the manhole prying up on windy days.

I am not like that at all, he said, as the man with the birthmark came over to his table and sat down opposite him.

'I thought you were going,' the man said. 'You told me you were going. You've been here an hour now.'

'I saw you,' Samuel said.

'I know you saw me. You must have seen me, mustn't you, because you were looking at me,' the man said. 'Not that I want the twopence, I've got a house full of furniture. Three rooms full to the ceiling. I've got enough chairs for everyone in Paddington to have a sit down. Twopence is twopence,' he said.

'But it was twopence to the waitress, too.'

'She's got sixpence now, hasn't she? She's made fourpence clear. It doesn't do any harm to you just because she thinks you were trying to nip it off her.'

'It was my sixpence.'

The man raised his hands. The palms were covered with calculations in ink. 'And they talk about equality. Does it matter whose sixpence it was? It might have been mine or anybody's. There was talk of calling the manageress,' he said, 'but I put my foot down there.'

They were both silent for several minutes.

'Made up your mind where you're going when you move out of here?' the man said at last. 'Because move you must, some time, you know.'

'I don't know where I'm going. I haven't any idea in the world. That's why I came up to London.'

'Look here,' the man said, controlling his voice, 'there's sense in everything. There's bound to be. Otherwise we wouldn't be able to carry on, would we? Everybody knows where he's going, especially if he's come by train. Otherwise he wouldn't move from where he took the train from. That's elementary.'

'People run away.'

'Have you run away?'

'No.'

'Then don't say it. Don't say it.' His voice trembled; he looked at the figures on his palms. Then gently and patiently he began again. 'Let's get the first thing straight. People who have come must go. People must know where they're going, otherwise the world could not be conducted on a sane basis. The streets would be full of people just wandering about, wouldn't they? Wandering about and having useless arguments with people who know where they're going. My name is Allingham, I live in Sewell Street off Praed Street, and I'm a furniture dealer. That's simple, isn't it? There's no need to complicate things if you keep your head and know who you are.'

'I'm Samuel Bennet. I don't live anywhere at all. I don't do any work, either.'

'Where are you going to go, then? I'm not a nosy parker, I told you my business.'

'I don't know.'

'He doesn't know,' Mr Allingham said. 'Don't think you're

anywhere now, mind. You can't call this place anywhere, can you? It's breathing space.'

'I've been wondering what was going to happen. That's what I've been discussing with myself. I came up really to see what would happen to me. I don't want to make anything happen myself.'

'He was discussing it with himself. With a boy of twenty. How old are you?'

'Twenty.'

'That's right. Discussing a question like that with a boy just out of his teens. What did you expect to happen?'

'I don't know. Perhaps people would come up and talk to me at the beginning. Women,' Samuel said.

'Why should they talk to you? Why should I talk to you? You're not going anywhere. You're not doing anything. You don't exist,' he said.

But all Samuel's strength was in his belly and his eyes. He should veil his eyes or the marble-topped counter might melt and all the clothes of the girls behind them peel away and all the cups chip on the shelves.

'Anyone might come up,' he said. Then he thought of his fine beginning. 'Anyone,' he said without hope.

A clerk from the Crescent a dozen doors away; a cold, ordinary woman from Birmingham, driven off by a wink; anybody, anybody; a deacon from the Valleys on a mean blind, with his pocket-book sewn in his combs; an elderly female assistant on holiday from a flannel and calico shop where the change hums on wires. Nobody he had ever wanted.

'Oh, anyone of course, Janet Gaynor,' Mr Allingham said. 'Marion Davies and Kay Francis and . . .'

'You don't understand. I don't expect that kind of person. I don't know what I do expect at all, but it isn't that.'

'Modest.'

'No, I'm not modest either. I don't believe in modesty. It's just that here I am and I don't know where to go. I don't want to know where to go.'

Mr Allingham began to plead, leaning across the table, pulling softly at Samuel's collar, showing the sums on his hands. 'Don't say you don't want to know where to go. Please. There's a good boy. We must take things easy, mustn't we? We mustn't complicate things. Take one simple question. Now don't rush it. Take your own time.' He gripped a teaspoon with one hand. 'Where will you be tonight?'

'I don't know. I'll be somewhere else but it won't be anywhere I've chosen because I'm not going to choose anything.'

Mr Allingham put the knotted teaspoon down.

'What do you want, Samuel?' he whispered.

'I don't know.' Samuel touched his breast pocket where his wallet was. 'I know I want to find Lucille Harris,' he said.

'Who's Lucille Harris?'

Then Mr Allingham looked at him.

'He doesn't know,' he said. 'Oh, he doesn't know!'

A man and a woman sat down at the next table.

'But you promised you'd destroy him,' the woman said.

'I'll do it, I'll do it,' the man said. 'Don't you worry. You drink your tea. Don't you worry.'

They had lived a long time together, and had grown to resemble one another with their dry, bunched faces and their nibbling mouths. The woman scratched herself as she drank, as she gripped the edge of the cup with her grey lips and shook it.

'Twopence she's got a tail,' Samuel said in a low voice, but Mr Allingham had not noticed them arrive.

'That's right,' he said. 'You have it your own way. And she's covered all over with fur.'

Samuel put his little finger in the neck of the empty bottle.

'I resign myself,' Mr. Allingham said.

'But you don't understand, Mr. Allingham.'

'I understand enough,' he said loudly. The couple at the next table stopped talking. 'You don't want to make things happen, don't you? I'll make them happen all right. You can't

come in here and talk to me like you've been talking. Lucille
Harris. Lucy da monk!'

The man and the woman began whispering. 'And it's only
half-past one,' the woman said. She shook her cup like a rat.

'Come on. We're going.' Mr Allingham scraped back his
chair.

'Where to?'

'Never you mind. It's I'm making things happen, isn't it?'

'I can't get my finger out of the bottle,' Samuel said.

Mr Allingham lifted up the suitcases and stood up. 'What's a
little bottle?' he said. 'Bring it with you, son.'

'Father and son, too,' the woman said as Samuel followed
him out.

The bottle hung heavily on his finger.

'Where now?' Outside in the roaring station.

'You follow me. And put your hand in your pocket. It looks
silly.'

As they walked up the slope to the street, Mr Allingham said,
'I've never been with anybody with a bottle on his finger
before. Nobody else has ever had a bottle on his finger. What'd
you want to put your finger in the bottle for?'

'I just pushed it in. I'll be able to get it off with soap, there's
no need to make a fuss.'

'Nobody else has ever had to get a bottle off with soap, that's
all I'm saying. This is Praed Street.'

'It's dull, isn't it?'

'All the horses have gone away,' Mr Allingham said. 'This is
my street. This is Sewell Street. It's dull, isn't it?'

'It's like the streets at home.'

A boy passed them and shouted 'Ikey Mo' to Mr Allingham.
'This is 23. See? There's the sign, 23.'

Mr Allingham opened the front door with a key. 'Second
floor, first on the right.'

He gave three knocks. 'Mr Allingham,' he said, and they
walked in.

The room was full of furniture.

CHAPTER II

PLENTY OF FURNITURE

EVERY INCH of the room was covered with furniture. Chairs stood on couches that lay on tables; mirrors nearly the height of the door were propped, back to back, against the walls, reflecting and making endless the hills of desks and chairs with their legs in the air, sideboards, dressing-tables, chests-of-drawers, more mirrors, empty bookcases, washbasins, clothes cupboards. There was a double bed, carefully made, with the ends of the sheets turned back, lying on top of a dining table on top of another table; there were electric lamps and lampshades, trays and vases, lavatory bowls and basins, heaped in the arm-chairs that stood on cupboards and tables and beds, touching the ceiling. The one window, looking out on the road, could just be seen through the curved legs of sideboards on their backs. The walls behind the standing mirrors were thick with pictures and picture frames.

Mr Allingham climbed into the room over a stack of mattresses, then disappeared.

'Hop in, boy.' His voice came up from behind a high kitchen dresser hung with carpets; and, climbing over, Samuel looked down to see him seated on a chair on a couch, leaning back comfortably, his elbow on the shoulder of a statue.

'It's a pity we can't cook here,' Mr Allingham said. 'There's plenty of stoves, too. That's a meat-safe,' he said, pointing to one corner. 'Just under the bedroom suite.'

'Have you got a piano?'

'There used to be one,' he said. 'I think it's in the other room. She put carpet over it. Can you play?'

'I can vamp. You can tell what tunes I'm doing, easily. Is the other room like this?'

'Two more rooms, but I think the piano's locked. Yes, there's plenty of furniture,' Mr Allingham said, looking round with distaste. 'Whenever I say "That's enough now," in she comes with her "Plenty more room, plenty more room." She'll find she can't get in one day, that's what'll happen. Or she can't get out; I don't know which would be the worst. It gets you sometimes you know,' he said, 'all this furniture.'

'Is she your wife, Mr Allingham?'

'She'll find there's a limit to everything. You get to feel kind of trapped.'

'Do you sleep here?'

'Up there. It's nearly twelve foot high. I've measured. I can touch the ceiling when I wake up.'

'I like this room,' Samuel said. 'I think it's perhaps the best room I've ever seen.'

'That's why I brought you. I thought you'd like it. Proper little den for a man with a bottle on his finger, isn't it? I told you, you're not like anybody else. Nobody else can bear the sight of it. Got your cases safe?'

'They're there. In the bath.'

'You keep your eye on them, that's all. I've lost a sofa. One more suite and I'll lose my bed. And what happens when a customer comes? I'll tell you. He takes one peek through the door and off he trots. You can only buy what's on the top at the moment, see.'

'Can you get into the other rooms?'

'You can,' Mr Allingham said. 'She takes a dive in, head-first. I've lost all interest in the other rooms, myself. You could live and die in there and nobody'd know. There's some nice Chippendale, too. Up by the skylight.'

He rested his other elbow on a hallstand.

'I got to feel lost,' he said. 'That's why I go down to the buffet; there's only tables and chairs there.'

Samuel sat on his perch, swinging the bottle and drumming his feet against the side of a bath mounted yards above the floor of mattresses. A carpet behind him, laid out flat and wide along the air, having no visible support, bore a great earthenware jar dangerously upon the backs of its patterned birds. High over his head, in the tall room, a rocking-chair balanced on a card-table, and the table's thin legs rested on the top of a cupboard standing up straight among pillows and fenders, with its mirrored door wide open.

'Aren't you frightened of things falling? Look at that rocking-chair. One little prod and over she comes.'

'Don't you dare. Of course I'm frightened,' Mr Allingham said. 'If you open a drawer over there, a wash-stand falls down over here. You've got to be quick as a snake. There's nothing on the top you'd like to buy, is there?'

'I like a lot of the things, but I haven't any money.'

'No, no, you wouldn't have money. That's right. Other people have money.'

'I like the big jar. You could hide a man in that. Have you got any soap for my finger?'

'Of course there's no soap, there's only wash-basins. You can't have a bath, either, and there's five baths. Why do you want a jar big enough to hide a man in? Nobody I've ever met wants to hide a man in a jar. Everybody else says that jar's too big for anything. Why do you want to find Lucille Harris, Sam?'

'I didn't mean I wanted to hide a man in it. I mean that you could if you wanted to. Oh, a man I know told me about Lucille, Mr Allingham. I don't know why I want to find her, but that's the only London address I kept. I put the others down the lavatory in the train. When the train was moving.'

'Good, good.' Mr Allingham put his hand on the thick, white neck of the naked statue, and tightened his fingers.

The door opened on to the landing. Two people came in, and climbed up the mattresses without a word. The first, a fat, short woman with black hair and a Spanish comb, who had painted her face as though it were a wall, took a sudden dive towards the corner behind Samuel and disappeared between two columns of chairs. She must have landed on cushions or a bed, for she made no sound. The second visitor was a tall, youngish man with a fixed smile; his teeth were large, like a horse's, but very white; his glistening fair hair was done in tight curls, and it smelt across the room. He stood on a spring mattress just inside the door, bouncing up and down. 'Come on, Rose, don't be sulky,' he said. 'I know where you've gone.' Then, pretending to see Samuel for the first time, 'Good gracious you look like a bird up there,' he said. 'Is Donald hiding anywhere?'

'I'm not hiding,' Mr Allingham said. 'I'm by the statue. Sam Bennet, George Ring.'

George Ring bowed and bounced, rising a foot from the mattress.

He and Mr Allingham could not see each other. Nobody could see the woman with the Spanish comb.

'I hope you've excused the room to Mr Bennet,' George Ring said. He bounced a few steps in the direction of the hidden statue.

'I don't think it needs any excusing, Mr Ring,' Samuel said. 'I've never seen such a comfortable room.'

'Oh, but it's terrible.' George Ring was moving up and down rapidly now. 'It's very kind of you to say it's comfortable, but look at the confusion. Just think of living here. You've got something on your finger, did you know that? Three guesses. It's a bottle.' He shook his curls and laughed as he bounced.

'You don't know anything yet,' said Mr Allingham's voice. The heavy bouncing had shaken down a carpet on to the hallstand and he was hidden as though in another, lower room. 'You don't know anything about him. You wait. What are you bouncing for, George? People don't go bouncing about like a ball as soon as they come into a room.'

'What don't I know about you?' In one leap George Ring was standing directly below Samuel, craning up his curls.

'He doesn't know where he's going, for one thing. And he's looking for a girl he doesn't know called Lucille.'

'Why are you looking for her?' George Ring's head touched the bath. 'Did you see her picture in the paper?'

'No, I don't know anything about her, but I want to see her because she's the only person I know by name in London.'

'Now you know two more, don't you? Are you sure you don't love her?'

'Of course I'm sure.'

'I thought perhaps she might be a sort of Holy Grail. You know what I mean. A sort of ideal.

'Go on, you big pussycat,' Mr Allingham said. 'Get me out of here.'

'Is this the first time you've come to London? I felt like that when I came up first, too. Years and years ago. I felt there was something I must find, I can't explain it. Something just round the corner. I searched and searched. I was so innocent. I felt like a sort of knight.'

'Get me out of here,' Mr Allingham said. 'I feel like the whole room's on top of me.'

'I never found it.' George Ring laughed and sighed and stroked the side of the bath. 'Perhaps you'll be lucky,' he said. 'You'll walk round the corner and there she'll be. Lucille. Lucille. Is she on the telephone?'

'Yes. I've got her number in my book.'

'Oh, that makes it easier, doesn't it. Come on, Rose,' he said. 'I know exactly where you are. She's in a pet.'

Samuel rocked softly on his box in the middle of the furniture. This was the fullest room in England. How many hundreds of houses had been spilt in here, tables and chairs coming in on a wooden flood, chests and cupboards soaring on ropes through the window and settling down like birds. The other rooms, beyond that jostled door, would be taller and darker even than this, with the mute, black shape of the locked piano mountainous under a shroud of carpets and Rose, with her comb like the prow of a ship, driving into their darkness and lying all night motionless and silent where she struck. Now she was dead still on a sunk bed between the column of chairs, buried alive, soft and fat and lost in a grave in a house.

'I'm going to buy a hammock,' George Ring said. 'I can't bear sleeping under all this furniture.'

Perhaps the room was crowded at night with people who could not see each other, stretched under chairs, under sofas, dizzily asleep on the tops of raised tables, waking up every morning and crying out, 'Earthquake, earthquake!'

'And then I'll go to bed like a sailor.'

'Tell Rose to come and get me out of here,' Mr Allingham said, behind the cloaked hallstand, 'I want to eat.'

'She's sulking Donald. She's mad about a Japanese screen now.'

'Do you hear that, Sam? Isn't there enough privacy in this room? Anybody can do anything, nobody can see you. I want to eat. I want to have a snack at Dacey's. Are you sleeping here tonight?'

'Who?' Samuel asked. 'Me?'

'You can doss down in one of the other rooms, if you think you can get up again. There's enough beds for a harem.'

'Harem,' George Ring said, pronouncing it another way. 'You've got company, Rose darling. Do come out and be introduced.'

'Thank you, Mr Allingham,' Samuel said.

'Didn't you really have any idea at all?' George Ring bounced, and for a moment his scented head was level with Samuel's. One wide, bright, horse-toothed smile, and the head was gone. 'About sleeping and things. I think it's awfully brave. You might have fallen in with all kinds of people. "He fell among thieves." Do you know Sir Henry Newbolt's poem?'

'He flung his empty revolver down the slope,' Samuel said.

The day was moving carelessly on to a promised end and in a dark room full of furniture where he'd lie down with his bunch of wives in a crow's-nest bed or rock them in a hammock under the ceiling.

'Goodie goodie! It's so exciting to find someone who knows about poetry. "The voices faded and the hills slept." Isn't that beautiful? The voices faded . . .? I can read poetry for hours, can't I, Donald? I don't care what kind of poetry it is, I love it all. Do you know, "Is there anybody there, said the traveller?" Where do you put the emphasis, Mr Bennet? Can I call you Sam? Do you say, "Is there *anybody* there" or "Is there anybody *there*"?'

'It isn't natural,' Mr Allingham said, 'for a man not to be able to see anybody when he's sitting right next to them. I'm not grumbling, but I can't see anything, that's all. It's like not being in the room.'

'Oh, do be quiet, Donald. Sam and I are having a perfectly serious discussion. Of course you're in the room, don't be morbid.'

'I think I'd put about the same emphasis on all the words,' Samuel said.

'But don't you find it tends to make the line rather flat? "*Is* there anybody there, said the traveller,"' George Ring murmured, pacing the mattresses, his head on one side. 'I feel you do want a stress somewhere.'

Will I be alone tonight in the room with the piano? Samuel wondered. Alone like a man in a warehouse, lying on each bed in turn, opening cupboards and putting my hand in, looking at myself in mirrors in the dark.

'Don't you call me morbid, George Ring,' Mr Allingham said. He tried to move, but the statue fell against his chair. 'I remember once I drank forty-nine Guinnesses straight off and I came home on the top of a bus. There's nothing morbid about a man who can do that. Right on the top of the bus, too, not just in the upper deck.'

Or will the room be full as a cemetery, but with the invisible dead breathing and snoring all around me, making love in the cupboards, drunk as tailors in the dry baths? Suddenly a warm body might dive in through the door and lie in my bed all night without a name or a word.

'I think forty-nine Guinnesses is piggish,' said George Ring.

'It was raining,' Mr Allingham said, 'and I never get truculent. I may sing and I may have a bit of a dance, but I never get nasty. Give me a hand, Sam.'

Samuel took the carpet off the hallstand and pushed the statue away. It had fallen between Mr Allingham's legs. He came up slowly into sight and rubbed his eyes like a man waking.

'I told you,' he said, 'you get trapped. Coming to Dacey's, George?'

'I'll have to stay for hours, you know that,' George Ring said. 'You know I'm the only person who can humour Rosie when she's in one of her states. Oh, come on, Rosie, don't be temperamental. It's ninety per cent temper and ten per cent mental. Just because you're an actress you think you can stay under the furniture all the afternoon. I'll count five . . .

Samuel followed Mr Allingham to the door.

'Five, six, seven,' George Ring said, as Mr Allingham slammed the door hard, and his voice was lost in the noise of furniture falling. They went down the stairs into the hallway that smelt of cabbage, and out on to the grey street.

'I think it must have been the rocking-chair,' Samuel said.

'Mrs Dacey's is just round the corner,' Mr Allingham said. 'There you are. See the Cadbury sign?' . . .

CHAPTER III

FOUR LOST SOULS

I

'Fun!' George Ring said.

They walked out of Sewell Street into Praed Street arm-in-arm.

'I'm a fool for the rain.' He shook his clinging curls and danced a few steps on the pavement.

'My new brown overcoat's in the bathroom,' Samuel said, and Mrs Dacey covered him with her umbrella.

'Go on, you're not the sort that puts a coat on in the rain, are you? Stop dancing, George.'

But George Ring danced down the pavement in the flying rain and pulled the others with him; unwillingly they broke into a dancing run under the lamp-posts' drizzle of light, Mrs Dacey, black as a deacon, jumping high over the puddles with a rustle and creak, Mr Allingham, on the outside, stamping and dodging along the gutter, Samuel gliding light and dizzy with his feet hardly touching the ground.

'Look out. People,' cried Mr Allingham, and dragged them, still dancing, out on to the slippery street. Caught in a circle of headlights and chased by horns, they stamped and scampered on to the pavement again, clinging fast to each other, their faces glistening, cold and wet.

'Where's the fire, George? Go easy, boy, go easy.' But Mr Allingham, one foot in the gutter, was hopping along like a rabbit and tugging at George Ring's arm to make him dance faster. 'It's all Sam's fault,' he said as he hopped, and his voice was high and loud like a boy's in the rain.

Look at London flying by me, buses and glow-worms, umbrellas and lamp posts, cigarettes and eyes under the water doorways, I am dancing with three strangers down Edgware Road in the rain, cried Samuel to the gliding boy around him. Light and without will as a suit of feathers, he held on to their arms, and the umbrella rode above them like a bird.

Cold and unsmiling, Mrs Dacey skipped by his side, seeing nothing through her misted glasses.

And George Ring sang as he bounced, with his drenched hair rising and falling in level waves, 'Here we go gathering nuts and may, Donald and Mrs Dacey and George and Sam.'

When they stopped, outside the Antelope, Mr Allingham leaned against the wall and coughed until he cried. All the time he coughed he never removed his cigarette.

'I haven't run for forty years,' he said, his shoulders shaking, and his handkerchief like a flag to his mouth. He led them into the Saloon Bar, where three young women sat with their shoes off in front of the electric log fire.

'Three whiskies. What's yours, Sam? Nice drop of Kiwi?'

'He'll have whisky, too,' Mrs Dacey said. 'See, he's got his colour back.'

'Kiwi's boot-polish,' one of the young women whispered, and she bent, giggling, over the grate. Her big toe came out of a hole in her stocking, suddenly, like a cold inquisitive nose, and she giggled again.

This was a bar in London. Dear Peggy, Samuel wrote with his finger on the counter, I am drinking in a bar called the Antelope in Edgware Road with a furniture dealer, the proprietress of a tea-shop, three young women and George Ring. I have put these facts down clearly because the scent I drank in the bath is still troublesome and people will not keep still. I am quite well but I do not know for how long.

'What're you doing, Sam? Looks like you're drawing. I've got a proper graveyard in my chest, haven't I? Cough, cough,' Mr Allingham said, angrily between each cough.

'It wasn't the cough that carried him off,' the young woman said. Her whole plump body was wriggling.

Everything is very trivial, Samuel wrote. Mr Allingham is drunk on one whisky. All his face goes pale except his mark.

'Here we are,' Mr Allingham said, 'four lost souls. What a place to put a man in.'

'The Antelope's charming,' said George Ring. 'There's some real hunting prints in the private bar.' He smiled at Sam and moved his long, blunt fingers rapidly along the counter as though he were playing a piano. 'I'm all rhythm. It's like a kind of current in me.'

'I mean the world. This is only a little tiny bit in it. This is all right, it's got regular hours; you can draw the curtains, you know what to expect here. But look at the world. You and your currents,' Mr Allingham said.

'No, really it's rippling out of me.' George Ring tap-danced with one foot and made a rhythmical, kissing noise with his tongue against the roof of his mouth.

'What a place to drop a man in. In the middle of streets and houses and traffic and people.'

The young woman wagged her finger at her toe. 'You be still.' Her friends were giggling now, covering their faces and peeping out at Mr Allingham between their fingers, telling each other to go on, saying 'hotcha' and 'hi de ho' and 'Minnie the Moocher's Wedding Day' as George Ring tapped one narrow, yellow buckskin shoe and strummed on the counter. They rolled their eyes and said, 'Swing it, sister,' then hissed again into a giggle.

'I've been nibbling away for fifty years now,' Mr Allingham said, 'and look at me. Look at me.' He took off his hat.

'There's hair,' whispered the young woman with the hole in her stocking.

His hair was the colour of ferrets and thin on the crown; it stopped growing at the temples but came out again from the ears. His hat made him a deep, white wrinkle on his forehead.

'Here we are nibbling away all day and night, Mrs Dacey. Nibble nibble.' His brown teeth came over his lip. 'No sense, no order, no nothing; we're all mad and nasty. Look at Sam there. There's a nice harmless boy, curly hair and big eyes and all. What's he do? Look at his bloody bottle.'

'No language,' said the woman behind the bar. She looked like a duchess, riding, rising and sinking slowly as she spoke, as though to the movements of a horse.

'Tantivy,' Samuel said, and blushed as Mr Allingham pointed a stained finger.

'That's right. Always the right word in the right place. Tantivy! I told you, people are all mad in the world. They don't know where they're going, they don't know why they're where they are; all they want is love and beer and sleep.'

'I wouldn't say no to the first,' said Mrs Dacey. 'Don't pay any attention to him,' she said to the woman behind the counter, 'he's a philosopher.'

'Calling everybody nasty,' said the woman, rising. 'There's people live in glass houses.' Over the hurdle she goes, thought Samuel idly, and she sank again on to the hidden saddle. She must do miles in a night, he said to his empty glass.

'People think about all kinds of other things.' George Ring looked at the ceiling for a vision. 'Music,' he said, 'and dancing.' He ran his fingers along the air and danced on his toes.

'Sex,' said Mr Allingham.

'Sex, sex, sex, it's always sex with you, Donald. You must be repressed or something.'

'Sex,' whispered the young woman by the fire.

'Sex is all right,' Mrs Dacey said. 'You leave sex alone.'

'Of course I'm repressed. I've been repressed for fifty years.'

'You leave sex out of it.' The woman behind the counter rose in a gallop. 'And religion,' she said.

Over she goes, clean as a whistle, over the hedge and the water-jump.

Samuel took a pound out of his wallet and pointed to the whisky on the shelf. He could not trust himself yet to speak to the riding woman with the stuffed, enormous bosom and two long milk-white loaves for arms. His throat was still on fire; the heat of the room blazed up his nostrils into his head, and all the

words at the tip of his tongue caught like petrol and gorse; he
saw three young women flickering by the metal logs, and his
three new friends thundered and gestured before him with the
terrible exaggeration of people of flesh and blood moving like
dramatic prisoners on a screen, doomed forever to enact their
pettiness in a magnified exhibition.

He said to himself: Mrs Antelope, pouring the whisky as
though it were four insults, believes that sex is a bed. The act
of love is an act of the bed itself; the springs cry 'Tumble' and
over she goes, horse and all. I can see her lying like a log on a
bed, listening with hate and disgust to the masterly voice of the
dented sheets.

He felt old and all-knowing and unsteady. His immediate
wisdom weighed so heavily that he clutched at the edge of the
counter and raised one arm, like a man trapped in the sea, to
signal his sinking.

'You may,' Mrs Dacey said, and the room giggled like a girl.

Now I know, thought Samuel beneath his load, as he
struggled to the surface, what is meant by a pillar of the church.
Long, cold Mrs Dacey could prop Bethesda on the remote top
of her carved head and freeze with her eyes the beetle-black
sinners where they scraped below her. Her joke boomed in the
roof.

'You've dropped a fiver, Sam.' Mr Allingham picked up a
piece of paper and held it out on the sun-stained palm of his
hand.

'It's Lucille Harris's address,' Samuel said.

'Why don't you give her a ring? The phone's on the stairs,
up there.' George Ring pointed. 'Outside the Ladies.'

Samuel parted a curtain and mounted.

'*Outside* the Ladies,' a voice said from the sinking room.

He read the instructions above the telephone, put in two
pennies, dialled, and said, 'Miss Harris? I'm a friend of
Austin's.'

'I am a friend of nobody's. I am detached,' he whispered
into the buzzing receiver. 'I am Lopo the outlaw, loping through

the night, companion of owls and murderers. Tu wit to woo,'
he said aloud into the mouthpiece.

She did not answer, and he shuffled down the stairs, swung
open the curtain, and entered the bright bar with a loping
stride.

The three young women had gone. He looked at the grate to
see if their shoes were still there, but they had gone too. People
leave nothing.

'She must have been out,' he said.

'We heard,' said Mr Allingham. 'We heard you talking to
her owl.' He raised his glass and stared at it, standing sadly
and savagely in the middle of the room, like a man with oblivion
in his hand. Then he made his choice, and drank.

'We're going places,' he said. 'We're taking a taxi and Sam is
going to pay for it. We're going to the West End to look for
Lucille.'

'I knew she was a kind of Holy Grail,' George Ring said
when they were all in the darkness of the taxi rattling through
the rain.

Samuel felt Mrs Dacey's hand on his knee.

'Four knights at arms, it's terribly exciting. We'll call at the
Gayspot first, then the Cheerioh, then the Neptune.'

'Four lost souls.'

The hand ached on along the thigh, five dry fishes dying on a
cloth.

'Marble Arch,' Mr Allingham said. 'This is where the fairies
come out in the moon.'

And the hurrying crowd in the rain might have had no flesh
or blood.

'Park Lane.'

The crowd slid past the bonnet and the windows, mixed their
faces with no features and their liquid bodies under a sudden
blaze, or vanished into the streaming light of a tall door that led
into the bowels of rich night London where all the women wore
pearls and pricked their arms with needles.

A car backfired.

'Hear the champagne corks?'

Mr Allingham is listening to my head, Samuel thought as he drew away from the fingers in the corner.

'Piccadilly. Come on Allingham's tour. That's the Ritz. Stop for a kipper, Sam?'

The Ritz is closed for ever. All the waiters would be bellowing behind their hands. Gustave, Gustave, cried a man in an opera hat, he is using the wrong fork. He is wearing a tie with elastic at the back. And a woman in evening dress cut so low he could see her navel with a diamond in it leaned over his table and pulled his bow tie out and let it fly back again to his throat.

'The filthy rich,' he said. My place is among the beggars and the outlaws. With power and violence Samuel Bennet destroys the whole artifice of society in his latest novel, *In the Bowels*.

'Piccadilly Circus. Centre of the world. See the man picking his nose under the lamp post? That's the Prime Minister.'

2

The Gayspot was like a coal cellar with a bar at one end, and several coalmen were dancing with their sacks. Samuel, at the door, swaying between Mrs Dacey and George Ring, felt his thigh, still frightened. He did not dare look down at it in case even the outside of the trouser-leg bore the inexcusable imprint of his terror in the taxi.

'It's cosmopolitan,' George Ring whispered. 'Look at the nigger.'

Samuel rubbed the night out of his eyes and saw the black men dancing with their women, twirling them among the green cane chairs, between the fruit machine and the Russian billiard table. Some of the women were white, and smoked as they danced. They pussed and spied around the room, unaware of their dancing, feeling the arms around them as though around the bodies of different women; their eyes were for the strangers entering, they went through the hot movements of the dance like women in the act of love, looking over men's shoulders at

their own remote and unconniving faces in a looking-glass.
The men were all teeth and bottom, flashers and shakers, with
little waists and wide shoulders, in double-breasted pin-stripe
and sleek, licked shoes, all ageless and unwrinkled, waiting for
the flesh-pot, proud and silent and friendly and hungry –
jerking round the smoking cellar under the centre of the world
to the music of a drum and a piano played by two pale white
cross boys whose lips were always moving.

As George Ring weaved Samuel through the dancers to the
bar they passed a machine and Samuel put in a penny for a
lemon. Out came one and sixpence.

'Who's going to win the Derby, Sam?' said Mr Allingham,
behind them.

'Isn't he a lucky poet?' George Ring said.

Mrs Dacey, in half a minute, had found a partner as tall as
herself and was dancing through the smoke like a chapel. He
had powdered his face to hide a scar from the corner of his eye
to his chin.

'Mrs Dacey's dancing with a razor-man,' Samuel said.

This was a breath and a scar of the London he had come to
catch. Look at the knickerless women enamouring from the
cane tables, waiting in the fumes for the country cousins to
stagger in, all savings and haywisps, or the rosy-cheeked old
men with buttonholes whose wives at home were as lively as
bags of sprouts. And the dancing cannibal-mouthed black razor
kings shaking their women's breasts and blood to the stutter of
the drums, snakily tailored in the shabby sweat-smelling jungle
under the wet pavement. And a crimped boy danced like a girl,
and the two girls serving were as harsh as men.

Mr Allingham bought four white wines. 'Go on. He did it
on a pin-table. You could bring your Auntie here, couldn't you,
Monica?' he said to the girl with the bow-tie pouring their
drinks.

'Not my Auntie,' Samuel said. Auntie Morgan Pont-Neath-
Vaughan in her elastic-sided boots. 'She doesn't drink,' he said.

'Show Monica your bottle. He's got a bottle on his finger.'

Samuel dug his hand deep in his jacket pocket. 'She doesn't want to see an old bottle.' His chest began to tickle as he spoke, and he slipped two fingers of his right hand between the buttons of his shirt on to his bare flesh. 'No vest,' he said in surprise, but the girl had turned away.

'It's a Sunday School,' Mr Allingham said. 'Tasted your wine yet, Sam? This horse's unfit to work. A regular little bun dance. You could bring the vicar's wife in here.'

Mrs Cotmore-Richards, four foot one and a squeak in her stockinged trotters.

'A regular little vestry,' Mr Allingham said. 'See that woman dancing? The one who fell in the flour-bin. She's a bank manager's niece.'

The woman with the dead white face smiled as she passed them in the arms of a padded boy.

'Hullo, Ikey.'

'Hullo, Lola. She's pretendin', see. Thinks she's Starr Faithfull.'

'Is she a prostitute, Mr Allingham?'

'She's a manicurist, Sammy. How's your cuticles? Don't you believe everything you see, especially after it's dark. This is all pretending. Look at Casanova there with the old girls. The last time he touched a woman he had a dummy in his mouth.'

Samuel turned around. George Ring whinnied in a corner with several women. Their voices shrilled and rasped through the cross noise of the drums.

'Lucy got a beating the last time I see her,' said a woman with false teeth and a bald fur. 'He said he was a chemist.'

'Lucille,' George Ring said, impatiently shaking his curls. 'Lucille Harris.'

'With a clothes-brush. He had it in a little bag.'

'There's a chemist,' said a woman wearing a picture hat.

'He doesn't mean Lucy Wakefield,' another woman said.

'Lucy Wakefield's in the Feathers with a man from Crouch End,' said the bank manager's niece, dancing past. The boy who danced with her was smiling with his eyes closed.

'Perhaps he got a leather belt in his little bag,' said the woman with the fur.

'It's all the same in a hundred years,' said the woman in the picture hat. She went down to her white wine, widening her legs like an old mule at a pool, and came up gasping. 'They put hair oil in it.'

This was all wrong. They spoke like the women who wore men's caps and carried fishfrails full of empties in the Jug and Bottle of the Compasses at home.

'Keeps away the dandruff.'

He did not expect that the nightclub women under the pavement should sing and twang like sirens or lure off his buttons with their dangerous, fringed violet eyes. London is not under the bedclothes where all the company is grand and vile by a flick of the cinema eye, and the warm linen doors are always open. But these women with the shabby faces and the comedians' tongues, squatting and squabbling over their mother's ruin, might have lurched in from Llanelly on a football night, on the arms of short men with leeks. The women at the tables, whom he had seen as enamouring shapes when he first came in dazed from the night, were dull as sisters, red-eyed and thick in the head with colds; they would sneeze when you kissed them or hiccup and say Manners in the dark traps of the hotel bedrooms.

'Good as gold,' he said to Mr Allingham. 'I thought you said this was a low place, like a speakeasy.'

'Speak easy yourself. They don't like being called low down here.' Mr Allingham leant close, speaking from the side of his mouth. 'They're too low for that. It's a regular little hell-hole,' he whispered. 'It's just warming up. They take their clothes off soon and do the hula hula; you'll like that.'

'Nobody knows Lucille,' George Ring said. 'Are you sure she isn't Lucy? There's a lovely Lucy.'

'No, Lucille.'

'"She dwells beside the springs of Dove." I think I like

Wordsworth better than Walter de la Mare sometimes. Do you know "Tintern Abbey"?'

Mrs Dacey appeared at Samuel's shoulder. 'Doesn't baby dance?' He shuddered at the cold touch of her hand on his neck. Not here. Not now. That terrible impersonal Bethesda rape of the fingers. He remembered that she had carried her umbrella even while she danced.

'I got a sister in Tintern,' said a man behind them.

'Tintern Abbey.' George Ring pouted and did not turn round.

'Not in the Abbey, she's a waitress.'

'We were talking about a poem.'

'She's not a bloody nun,' the man said.

The music stopped, but the two boys on the little platform still moved their hands and lips, beating out the dance in silence.

Mr Allingham raised his fist. 'Say that again and I'll knock you down.'

'I'll blow you down,' the man said. He puffed up his cheeks, and blew. His breath smelt of cloves.

'Now, now.' Mrs Dacey levelled her umbrella.

'People shouldn't go around insulting nuns then,' Mr Allingham said as the ferrule tapped his waistcoat.

'I'll blow you down,' the man said. 'I never insulted any nun. I've never spoken to a nun.'

'Now, now.' The umbrella drove for his eyes, and he ducked.

'You blow again,' said Mrs Dacey politely, 'I'll push it up your snout and open it.'

'Don't you loathe violence,' George Ring said. 'I've always been a terrible pacifist. One drop of blood and I feel slimy all over. Shall we dance?'

He put his arm round Samuel's waist and danced him away from the bar. The band began again though none of the couples had stopped dancing.

'But we're two men,' Samuel said. 'Is this a waltz?'

'They never play waltzes here, it's just self-expression. Look, there's two other men dancing.'

'I thought they were girls.'

'My friend thought you were a couple of girls,' George Ring said in a loud voice as they danced past them. Samuel looked at the floor, trying to follow the movements of George Ring's feet. One, two, three, turn around, tap.

One of the young men squealed, 'Come up and see my Aga Cooker.'

One, two, three, swirl and tap.

'What sort of a girl is Polly Dacey, really? Is she mad?'

I'm like thistledown, thought Samuel. Swirl about and swirl again, on the toes now, shake those hips.

'Not so heavy, Sam. You're like a little Jumbo. When she went to school she used to post mice in the pillar-box and they ate up all the letters. And she used to do things to boys in the scullery. I can't tell you. You could hear them screaming all over the house.'

But Samuel was not listening any more. He circled and stumbled to a rhythm of his own among the flying legs, dipped and retreated, hopped on one leg and spun, his hair falling over his eyes and his bottle swinging. He clung to George Ring's shoulder and zig-zagged away from him, then bounced up close again.

'Don't swing the bottle. Don't swing it. Look out. Sam. Sam.'

Samuel's arm flew back and a small woman went down. She grabbed at his legs and he brought George Ring with him. Another man fell, catching fast to his partner's skirt. A long rip and she tumbled among them, her legs in the air, her head in a heave of bellies and arms.

Samuel lay still. His mouth pressed on the curls at the nape of the neck of the woman who had fallen first. He put out his tongue.

'Get off my head; you've got keys in your pocket.'

'Oh, my leg!'

'That's right. Easy does it. Upsadaisy.'

'Someone's licking me,' cried the woman at the bottom.

Then the two girls from behind the bar were standing over them, slapping and kicking, pulling them up by the hair.

'It was that one's fault. He crowned her with a bottle. I saw him,' said the bank manager's niece.

'Where'd he get the bottle from, Lola?'

The girl with the bow tie dragged Samuel up by the collar and pointed to his left hand. He tried to slip it in his pocket but a hand like a black boxing glove closed over the bottle. A large black face bent down and stared into his. He saw only the whites of the eyes and the teeth.

I don't want a cut on my face. Don't cut my lips open. They only use razors in stories. Don't let him have read any stories.

'Now, now,' said Mrs Dacey's voice. The black face jerked back as she thrust out her opened umbrella, and Samuel's hand was free.

'Throw him out, Monica.'

'He was dancing like a monkey, throw him out.'

'If you throw him out you can throw me out too,' Mr Allingham said from the bar. He raised his fists.

Two men walked over to him.

'Mind my glasses.' He did not wear any.

They opened the door and threw him up the steps.

'Bloody nun,' a voice shouted.

'Now you.'

'And the old girl. Look out for her brolly, Dodie.'

Samuel fell on the area step below Mr Allingham, and Mrs Dacey came flying after with her umbrella held high.

It was still raining heavily.

3

'Just a passing call,' said Mr Allingham. As though he were sitting indoors at a window, he put out his hand to feel the rain. Shoes slopped past on the pavement above his head. Wet trousers and stockings almost touched the brim of his hat. 'Just in and out,' he said. 'Where's George?'

I've been bounced, Samuel thought.

'It reminds me of my old man.' Mrs Dacey's face was hidden under the umbrella, as though in a private, accompanying thunder cloud. 'In and out, in and out. Just one look at him, and out he went like clockwork.'

Oh, the Gayspot? Can't go there, old man. Samuel winked seriously in the dark. Oh, carrying a cargo. Swinging a bottle around. One look at me, out I went.

'He used to carry a little book with all the places he couldn't go to and he went to them every Saturday.'

Fool, fool, fool, Samuel said to himself.

The steps were suddenly lit up as the door opened for George Ring. He came out carefully and tidily, to a rush of music and voices that faded at once with the vanishing of the smoky light, and stood on Mrs Dacey's step, his mane of curls golden against the fanlight, a god or a half-horse emerging from the under-world into the common rain.

'They're awfully cross,' he said. 'Mrs Cavanagh ripped her skirt and she didn't have anything on underneath. My dear, it's like Ancient Rome down there and now she's wearing a man's trousers and he's got legs exactly like a spider's. All black and hairy. Why are you sitting in the rain?'

'It's safe,' Mr Allingham said. 'It's nice and safe in the rain. It's nice and rational sitting on the steps in the rain. You can't knock a woman down with a bottle here. See the stars? That's Arcturus. That's the Great Bear. That's Sirius, see, the green one. I won't show you where Venus is. There's some people can't enjoy themselves unless they're knocking women down and licking them on the floor. They think the evening's wasted unless they've done that. I wish I was home. I wish I was lying in bed by the ceiling. I wish I was lying under the chairs like Rosie.'

'Who started to fight, anyway? Let's go round the corner to the Cheerioh.'

'That was ethical.'

They climbed up the street, George Ring first, then Mr Allingham, then Samuel and Mrs Dacey. She tucked his arm in hers.

'Don't you worry. You hold on to me. Cold? You're shivering.'

'It'll be Cheerioh all right.'

The Cheerioh was a bad blaze, an old hole of lights. In the dark, open a cupboard full of cast-off clothes moving in a wind from nowhere, the smell of mothballs and damp furs, and find a lamp lit, candles burning, a gramophone playing.

'No dancing for you,' Mr Allingham said. 'You need space. You want the Crystal Palace.'

Mrs Dacey still held Samuel by the arm. 'You're safe with me. I've taken a fancy,' she said. 'Once I take a fancy I never let go.'

'And never trust a woman who can't get up.' Mr Allingham pointed to a woman sitting in a chair by the Speedboat pin-table. 'She's trying to get up all the time.' The woman made a sudden movement of her shoulders. 'No, no, legs first.'

'This used to be the cow-shed,' George Ring said, 'and there was real straw on the floor.'

Mrs Dacey never lets go. Samuel saw the fancy shining behind her glasses, and in her hard mouse-trap mouth. Her cold hand hooked him. If he struggled and ran she would catch him in a corner and open her umbrella inside his nose.

'And real cows,' Mr Allington said.

The men and women drinking and dancing looked like the older brothers and sisters of the drinkers and dancers in the club round the corner, but no one was black. There were deep green faces, dipped in a sea dye, with painted cockles for mouths and lichenous hair, sealed on the cheeks; red and purple, slate-grey, tide-marked, rat-brown and stickily white-washed, with violet-inked eyes or lips the colour of Stilton; pink chopped, pink lidded, pink as the belly of a newborn monkey, nicotine yellow with mustard flecked eyes, rust scraping through the bleach, black hairs axle-greased down among the peroxide; squashed fly stubbles, saltcellared necks thick with pepper powder; carrot-heads, yolk-heads, black-heads, heads bald as sweetbreads.

'All white people here,' Samuel said.

'The salt of the eath,' Mr Allington said. 'The foul salt of the earth. Drunk as a pig. Ever seen a pig drunk? Ever seen a monkey dancing like a man? Look at that king of the animals. See him? The one who's eaten his lips. That one smiling. That one having his honeymoon on her feet.'

COMMENTARY

REMINISCENCES OF CHILDHOOD

This piece deals with early childhood and a young boy's widening knowledge of Swansea, the town where Thomas was born and went to school. The technique is impressionistic; we are given a series of quick vivid pictures, enlivened with imagery: 'we used to wander whistling through the packed streets, stale as station sandwiches'; 'we took a tram that shook like an iron jelly'. Yet there is not much in the way of adult comment, so that the total picture is one of innocence. It is a re-creation of the scents and sounds and sights of childhood, recounted in tumultuous language. By means of his ever-fertile wit and imagery Thomas offers us his experience intact, with all the freshness and impact of immediate happening. His imagination is verbal. One idea sparks off an associative train, which crackles along with undiminished energy until the end of the sentence. The prevailing mood of innocence can be caught by means of a phrase heavy with associations. Here is one which deliberately gives us a whiff of the Garden of Eden: '. . . an ancient keeper, known as Smoky, was the whispered snake in the grass one must keep off'. Paradise and the pride of the Parks Department are neatly and tellingly juxtaposed.

MEMORIES OF CHRISTMAS

Like the previous piece, 'Memories of Christmas' is reconstructed from the experiences of several years of childhood. The same technique is used but it is an altogether weightier piece. The author plays a much more positive part, controlling and ordering his memories according to the conventional chronology of Christmas. Like 'Reminiscences of Childhood', it was originally broadcast, and this greater coherence is the result of Thomas's awareness of the demands of radio as a medium.

The town here is, of course, Swansea.

A VISIT TO GRANDPA'S

This story combines elements often considered to be typical of Dylan Thomas. It is a mixture of remembered incidents, imagination and fantasy, set in the world of actuality. The places and people really exist, and no doubt Dylan Thomas did pay a visit to his Grandpa as a boy. But Grandpa's eccentricities become larger than life through the writer's lyrical portrait of him. He is comic, pompous and futile, until he is gripped by a sudden (and clearly recurrent) desire to prepare for death. Now he becomes as portentous for us as no doubt he seemed to his wondering grandson. We come to accept and value him beyond the face value that was set upon him earlier. We recognize him as a human soul.

A STORY

This piece is of interest in the development of Thomas's style and work because it shows an increasing ability to portray a community. Here we find the characters of a Welsh village, none of them stock characters, but, one feels, each one alive and drawn from life. The humour is contained in the characters and arises from them. There is verbal humour in the narration, but it is in the friction between people that comic heat is generated. As a piece of writing it foretells *Under Milk Wood*.

And yet, modifying the gusto, there is a sadness. '"Who goes there?" called out Will Sentry to the flying moon.' And why? we might well ask. Why the pub crawl, why the need for such an outing? What sort of life do we lead that we have to find an escape such as this? The question and answer are implicit in the piece.

PATRICIA, EDITH AND ARNOLD

Both Patricia and Edith are in love with being in love. The non-descript Arnold is the fantasy-object for them both. But even fantasy has its rules where love is concerned, and Arnold breaks them. So there is an awful (and highly satisfactory) row, and no doubt they'll go on much as before. Only the boy is alive to the pathos of the situation. His snowman – Arnold collapses when the perfidy is exposed; the real Arnold will in all probability bounce back.

EXTRAORDINARY LITTLE COUGH

Four boys – Dan, Sidney, Dylan and George Hooping (nick-named Cough) – go camping by the sea at Rhossilli. There they meet, with a dismay quite equal to their skill in concealing it, two older boys from their school, Brazell and Skully. Then the girls appear. The older boys monopolize the three girls, flirting and joking. The girls respond predictably. Dylan, romantic and self-absorbed, remains an outsider. He and Dan can tease little Cough, but they are outclassed by the older boys when it comes to girls. Also Brazell and Skully are far more expert and relent-less in their teasing of little Cough, extraordinary little Cough, who is prompted by their banter to take upon himself an extra-ordinary personal challenge. Perhaps little Cough is the only one of the group who acts according to his own individual needs. He is growing while the others are marking time.

THE FOLLOWERS

We had an inkling of how Dylan Thomas can capture the man-of-the-world conversation of boys in their late adolescence in the previous story. 'The Followers' goes deeper – it hits off precisely how young men, at a loss to know what to do and with no money to do it with, will wander round the town ostensibly in search of adventure, which they in fact keep at a safe distance. They play a schoolboy trick on one girl and follow another to her home, ex-changing fantasies of almost oriental amorousness, as they tramp the suburban pavements. They spy their houri through the kitchen window – all is as respectably dull as the streets through which they have come. But is there magic of another kind in this ordinary spot? The story's bizarre ending would have us believe so.

AFTER THE FAIR

This strange little story has an affinity with the Hunchback who is the subject of the poem in 'Reminiscences of Childhood'. It has a similar starting-point: a clear picture in the author's mind. As he says of the Hunchback: 'The face of the old man who sat summer and winter on the bench looking over the reservoir I can see clearly now, and I wrote a poem long long after I'd left the park and the sea-town'. The picture which seems to be the origin of 'After the Fair' is contained in the last paragraph. The characters become almost symbolic, an effect which is reinforced by the way they are named: the Fat Man, the girl in black, the baby. As they whirl round to the ever-increasing music, they are surrounded by the men from the caravans.

This picture, and the circumstances behind it as outlined in the story, can work in the mind. What do they represent, these people? Is the fair a miniature of society, with the girl the outsider? Does the story tell us something of humanity and the need for friendship and warmth? If the story is a parable, then what is the moral? If it is not a parable, but only an odd little incident, wherein lies its power?

THE VISITOR

'The Visitor' is about dying, and offers a vision of a man's last hours. Dylan Thomas was haunted by the idea of dying, and he distils his prevailing obsession into the four pages which make up this story. Of all his prose pieces, 'The Visitor' brings us closest to Thomas the poet.

THE INTERNATIONAL EISTEDDFOD

This piece is included as an example of Thomas's work which is not autobiographical. It was first given as a broadcast talk in 1953, and is representative of the journalistic element in Thomas's output, for there is no story thread, nor does it give us anything of Thomas's own experience. Here the impressionistic method is used purely for descriptive purposes, without any of the fantastic flights which are found elsewhere in his work.

THE INTERNATIONAL EISTEDDFOD is an arts festival incorporating a series of competitions which is held every year in Llangollen in North Wales. Choirs, dancers, instrumentalists and poets come from all over the world to take part.

LLANGOLLEN is a small town on the banks of the River Dee. DINAS BRAN is a ruined castle on the top of one of the hills overlooking the town.

ADVENTURES IN THE SKIN TRADE

This is the longest and most ambitious piece of prose writing which Thomas attempted, and it remained unfinished at his death.

Thomas intended the work to be autobiographical, not in the sense of a record of actual experiences, but rather the experiences of the dramatized self he used to imagine and describe. To understand how he did this it would be best to take an incident from his life At one point his father, worried by the amount Thomas was drinking, told him of his own history and how he had overcome near-alcoholism. There is no doubt that Thomas was shocked by this revelation of his father's, and equally no doubt that the tale he tells of falling over his drunken father's body in the aisle of a darkened church is a dramatization in fantasy of the original experience.

So too, are the adventures of his hero Samuel Bennet, who encounters in London the characters and experiences of Thomas's imagination. Reality is extended rather than thrown overboard, and the whole vein of the piece is comic and picaresque.

There is a serious artistic purpose to it, however. In the first chapter, 'A Fine Beginning', Samuel Bennet destroys his past. Symbolically, in the destruction and havoc he causes in the home, he breaks free from his parents, and on the train he destroys his notebook, his personal past. 'Home and help were over.' From this point on Bennet is passive. When he reaches London, 'the rest must come by accident.' He attracts adventures by his very passivity. Things happen to him, and he accepts them. He meets peculiar people and finds himself in some very peculiar situations. Then at some point he would find that he had shed a skin (see Introduction).

The key image of the work is of Samuel Bennet with a bottle on his finger. A bottle is made with the help of a craftsman's breath and is an image of poetry. The finger stuck into the bottle imprisons the hand, which is the instrument for writing poetry. At this level Samuel Bennet is Dylan Thomas, a queer sort of person wedded to the profession of poetry, which everywhere attracts attention. Here Thomas sees the absurdity of himself, and is at his most self-deprecating. Without the bottle Bennet would have been unremarked; with it he attracts the extraordinary adventures which are the subject of the tale. There are elements of allegory: a journey is made through London as through a modern inferno, and the poet is set apart from the rest of humanity by his unique gift.

Why was *Adventures in the Skin Trade* not finished? Vernon Watkins, one of Thomas's closest friends, suggests that there may be two reasons. The first is that Thomas, usually a meticulous and slow worker, mistrusted the speed and facility with which he found himself able to write this novel. The second is that when the Second World War broke out his vision was attracted again to poetry, and he abandoned prose in order to make poems about war and about childhood.

READING LIST

Biographical material and background reading

BRINNIN, JOHN MALCOLM *Dylan Thomas in America* (J. M. Dent 1956).

FITZGIBBON, CONSTANTINE *The Life of Dylan Thomas* (J. M. Dent 1965).

FITZGIBBON, CONSTANTINE (ed.) *Selected Letters of Dylan Thomas* (J. M. Dent 1966).

THOMAS, CATLIN *Leftover Life to Kill* (Putnam 1957).

WATKINS, VERNON (ed.) *Dylan Thomas: Letters to Vernon Watkins* (Faber & Faber 1957; Dent paperback 1965).

MAUD, RALPH *Poet in the Making: The Notebooks of Dylan Thomas* (J. M. Dent 1968).

The works of Dylan Thomas

Portrait of the Artist as a Young Dog (J. M. Dent 1940).

Deaths and Entrances (J. M. Dent Feb. 1946).

Collected Poems 1934–1952 (J. M. Dent 1955).

The Doctor and the Devils (J. M. Dent 1953).

Quite Early one Morning (J. M. Dent 1954).

Under Milk Wood (J. M. Dent 1954; Acting Edition 1958).

A Prospect of the Sea and Other Stories (J. M. Dent 1955).

Adventures in the Skin Trade (Putnam & Co. 1955).

Twenty Years a Growing (J. M. Dent 1964).

A Child's Christmas in Wales (New Directions 1954).

The following paperback editions and collections are published by Dent (Aldine Paperback Series)

Miscellany One.
Miscellany Two.
A Prospect of the Sea and Other Stories.
Portrait of the Artist as a Young Dog.
Quite Early One Morning.
Under Milk Wood.
Adventures in the Skin Trade.

RECORD LIST

The following recordings of Dylan Thomas reading his own works have been issued by Caedmon (all 12 in., 33⅓ rpm).

TC1002
Fern Hill; Child's Christmas in Wales; Do not go gentle into that good night; In the White Giant's thigh; Ballad of the long-legged bait; Ceremony after a fire-raid.

TC1018
Lament; Poems on his birthday; Should lanterns shine; There was a Saviour; Refusal to mourn; If I were tickled by the rib of love; And death shall have no dominion; Winter's Tale.

TC1043
A few words of a kind; On the marriage of a virgin; The hunchback in the park; Over Sir John's Hill; Light breaks where no sun shines; After the funeral; In country sleep.

TC1132
Quite early one morning; Reminiscences of childhood; A visit to Grandpa's; Holiday memory.

Caedmon also issue a recording of *Under Milk Wood* (12 in., 33⅓ rpm, original New York Cast) TC0996–7.

Richard Burton reads *A Selection from the Works of Dylan Thomas* on Argo RG43.